THE RISE OF MODERN SCIENCE

External or Internal Factors?

PROBLEMS IN EUROPEAN CIVILIZATION

THE RISE
OF
MODERN SCIENCE

External or Internal Factors?

EDITED WITH AN INTRODUCTION BY

George Basalla, UNIVERSITY OF TEXAS

D. C. HEATH AND COMPANY
Lexington, Massachusetts

Copyright © 1968 by D. C. Heath and Company

Printed in the United States of America

Library of Congress Number: 68-20418

Table of Contents

Introduction

MODERN SCIENCE is a product of Western civilization. It first appeared in Europe during the sixteenth and seventeenth centuries and then slowly spread to North and South America, Australia, Asia, and Africa. In this way the fruits of modern science were made more widely available to the world. These fruits included novel and fundamental insights into the operations of nature, a high level of material well-being, and, most recently, the possible destruction of all life on earth.

How did this vast enterprise of science get its start? What were the unique elements in the Western tradition that stimulated its creation and rapid growth? Did science emerge because of a mutation in the intellectual life of Europe or through a long developmental process? Does its origin and growth depend upon external factors — e.g., social and economic conditions — or upon factors from within science itself? These questions have perplexed historians for over a century. In attempting to answer them historians have turned to the histories of science, economics, religion, intellectualism, psychoanalysis, political ideology, art and the occult, and sociology.

Long before scholars formally recognized the rise of modern science as a legitimate historical problem, scientists and philosophers were speculating about it. Their speculations date to the sixteenth and seventeenth centuries and are characterized by a belief that modern science appeared around the time of the Renaissance, the period identified with the revival of ancient learning. It was generally assumed that this reawakening was in reaction to the preceding period which was marked by intellectual sterility and dominated by theology and excessive philosophizing.

Sir Francis Bacon, who compared the scholastics to spiders content to weave cobwebs of learning and ignore the material universe, is the best known of the early commentators on the genesis of modern science. But there were others — some more closely involved in scientific activity than Lord Chancellor Bacon. The German astronomer Johannes Kepler, for example, held that the world had slept for a thousand years after the fall of Rome and had only recently (1450) been awakened. Paracelsian medicine and Copernican astronomy were cited by Kepler as evidence of the awakening.

Additional proof of the belief in the recent origins of science is the proliferation of the word "new" in the titles and contents of scientific works of the sixteenth and seventeenth centuries. Science itself was known as the "new philosophy." Galileo's great treatise on mechanics was entitled *Discourses on Two New Sciences*. Kepler was the author of a *New Astronomy*. Bacon gave mankind a *Novum Organum* (New Logic) and the scientific utopia *New Atlantis*. Various others claimed to offer a "new" geometry, medicine, or chemistry.

When the men of the Enlightenment considered the origins of science they repeated the interpretation of the previous century. Immanuel Kant wrote that the experimental work of Galileo and Torricelli shed a new light upon the study of nature. D'Alembert, in the Preliminary Discourse to the *Encyclopédie*, called scholasticism "the so-called science of the centuries of ignorance"[1] and praised Newton, Galileo,

[1] Jean le Rond D'Alembert, *Preliminary Discourse to the Encyclopedia of Diderot*, trans. by Richard N. Schwab and Walter E. Rex (Indianapolis: Bobbs-Merrill, 1963), p. 71.

Harvey, Huygens, Bacon, and Descartes for being first to reveal the truths of the universe to mankind. Similar views are to be found in the writings of Voltaire, Condorcet, and Hume. All of these men were obliged to comment on the rise of science because science was considered to be the force that had brought enlightenment to the eighteenth century.

The Romantic reaction to Enlightenment thought resulted in the creation of a more sympathetic attitude toward the Middle Ages. Romantic historians and writers sentimentalized the ideals and people of that era, softening the dichotomy between the age of scholasticism and chivalry and the time of cultural rebirth. The study of the origins of modern science was neglected during this revolution in historiography because science was antithetical to many of the major premises of Romanticism and too closely identified with the optimistic materialism of the Enlightenment. Therefore, in 1837 when the English prelate and philosopher William Whewell published his history of the physical and biological sciences he drew upon the traditional interpretation of the emergence of modern science.

According to Whewell, scientific progress is dependent upon the ability of men of genius to formulate clear ideas and apply them to distinct facts. When this is done science flourishes and we have an Inductive Epoch. It is possible to have preludes and sequels to the Inductive Epochs and, since science is sometimes stagnant, we also find Stationary Periods. The Middle Ages is the prime example of a Stationary Period between the era of Greek science and the rise of modern science. Whewell spent over sixty pages tracing the causes of the "barrenness and darkness" of the Middle Ages, but he believed he had satisfactorily explained the birth of modern science in the five pages where he spoke of a possible connection between medieval architecture and the seventeenth-century science of mechanics.

Whewell was chosen to open this selection of readings because he was the first to attempt a comprehensive survey of the growth of scientific thought and because his book gained influence as a standard reference work. Little introduction or justification is needed for the second selection printed here. Jakob Burckhardt is generally known as the author of *The Civilization of the Renaissance in Italy,* a book outlining the modern conception of the Renaissance. Although Burckhardt was not particularly interested in the search for the origins of modern science he listed scientific activity as one more proof of the modernity of Renaissance Italian culture. The Italian people, wrote Burckhardt, took "a natural delight in the study and investigation of nature, at a time when other nations" were indifferent to it. He hinted that medieval science was stifled by a fear of nature and an addiction to books and tradition but avoided a detailed criticism of the Middle Ages. Like Whewell, Burckhardt offered a perfunctory explanation for the sudden emergence of science — the Italian mind, imbued with ancient learning and freed from its restraints, turned to the contemplation of the external world. Burckhardt's short analysis is not an original one. Its real significance lies in the fact that it formally identified the rise of modern science with the wider, and more complex, problem of the Renaissance.

Historians of medieval science offered the first historically-documented alternative to the traditional interpretation of the birth of modern science. Led by Pierre Duhem, a Franco-Catholic physicist and philosopher of science, the medievalists began a systematic study of science in the Middle Ages. In doing so they attacked the legend portraying the medieval era as a blank or stagnant period in the history of science. Duhem's detailed historical researches, published 1905–17, were undertaken to show that many of the fundamental principles of the science of Descartes, Galileo, and Newton could be traced to thirteenth- and fourteenth-century sources. In Duhem's view, modern science originated in the philosophical speculations of medieval thinkers; it was not a unique product of the sixteenth and seventeenth centuries.

Duhem's researches coincided with the birth of the history of science as a scholarly discipline, and his work was carried on by others in the profession. Lynn Thorndike, George Sarton, and Charles Homer Haskins are three older investigators of medieval science; Anneliese Maier, Marshall Clagett, and Alistair C. Crombie have made the most recent contributions to this field. These scholars have carefully reconstructed the medieval study of optics, motion, and mathematics and clarified the relationship between philosophy and science in the Middle Ages. Although Duhem's work remains as the source and inspiration for all later investigators of medieval science, his followers have been more critical than their master. They continue to search for medieval influences on early modern science, but they stress the medieval setting of those influences and no longer equate the principles of medieval science with their superficially similar modern counterparts. Crombie (p. 12), in his recent history of medieval science, has produced a synthesis of the views of Duhem and his critical successors.

After Duhem, partisans of the more recent origins of modern science could no longer portray the medieval period as a blight on the development of science. They could still argue, however, that the essential features of modern science were not evident until sometime in the sixteenth or seventeenth century. Critics of the medievalist stand were able to raise one important question: If the thinkers of the thirteenth and fourteenth centuries had a clear view of the fundamentals of modern science why don't we find a Copernicus, Galileo, or Newton in that era? In attempting to answer this question the medievalists isolated what they considered to be the intrinsic elements of modern science and claimed that medieval thinkers first uncovered these elements and made them available for eventual use by a Copernicus, Galileo, or Newton. Notice that the controversy has moved to subtler levels. It is no longer a matter of total ignorance of science opposed to a sudden flowering of modern science. The dispute now centers about what are the fundamental constituents of modern science and to what extent these constituents were evident, in their modern recognizable form, during the Middle Ages.

This conflict of views has not been settled in any definitive way. Most historians of science willingly acknowledge the significance of the medieval heritage of modern science but they cannot accept the proposition that modern science is merely an evolutionary extension of medieval science.

The next selection illustrates the Renaissance scholars' reply to the medievalists. The Copernican expert Edward Rosen gathered together Duhem's scattered references to the emergence of modern science and then argued that the inconsistencies, misinterpretations, and errors of the French philosopher destroyed his own position and restored the original Burckhardtian conception of Renaissance science.

Burckhardt finds another defender in the well-known Renaissance specialist Hans Baron. Baron wrote specifically to refute Dana B. Durand's[2] charges that fifteenth-century Italian science was largely derived from traditional medieval sources. Weighing the respective roles of "tradition" and "innovation" in Italian Renaissance science, Durand concluded that "tradition" prevailed. Baron defended Burckhardt by calling attention to broad intellectual and social innovations which are to be identified with the Quattrocento and which proved to be crucial to the subsequent development of modern science.

If modern science is not the end-product of a long evolutionary process dating back to the Middle Ages, but the result of a

[2] Hans Baron, "Toward a More Positive Evaluation of the Fifteenth-Century Renaissance," *Journal of the History of Ideas*, IV, no. 1 (1943); Dana B. Durand, "Tradition and Innovation in Fifteenth Century Italy," *Journal of the History of Ideas*, IV, no. 1 (1943).

mutation that occurred at the beginning of the modern period, then it is the historian's task to investigate this mutational change and reveal its causes. The wide variety of causal factors that have been proposed by historians are displayed in the remaining selections in this volume. Economic, social, and psychological changes, along with religion, art, occult thought, and philosophy, have been advanced as the sources of modern science. Ideological or religious preferences have sometimes motivated the historian's particular choice of a causal factor.

In 1894 Friedrich Engels wrote that the technical needs of society were far more important for the cultivation of science than ten universities. This epigrammatic statement summarizes the Marxist belief that science ultimately rests upon the economic structure of society. If the growth of science is dependent upon economic conditions, so is its origin. Engels alluded to the latter dependency and then criticized historians for writing as if science had "fallen from the skies."[3] But despite Engels' complaint, the Marxist-economic interpretation of the rise of science had little influence in the Western world prior to 1931.

From June 30 to July 4, 1931, the Second International Congress of the History of Science and Technology met in London. A large Soviet delegation, headed by the eminent Communist theorist Nikolai I. Bukharin, came to present the Marxist explanation for the development of science. Bukharin's paper, "Theory and Practice from the Standpoint of Dialectical Materialism," stressed the unity of science and technology and indicated the primacy of technology over science. What Bukharin had discussed theoretically, Professor Boris Hessen then presented concretely in an extraordinary paper that claimed that Newton's great masterpiece of mathematical physics, the *Principia*, was a product of seventeenth-century England's commercial and industrial activity and the social system associated with it.[4] In developing his thesis, Hessen asserted that the scientific activity of the sixteenth and seventeenth centuries could be traced to the technical needs of Europe's newly emerging bourgeoisie.

Hessen is presented in this volume without an accompanying criticism or refutation. His appraisal of medieval culture and economy is so biased and ill-informed that its faults are self-evident. However, it is difficult for the layman to see flaws when the argument turns to the question of scientific progress and technological needs. The historian of science would have to analyze each case cited by Hessen and prove the contrary to be true. This has been partially accomplished in several books and articles, and there is general agreement that Hessen distorted historical facts to fit his ideological mold. But although he has been severely challenged by his critics, Hessen's work has led more judicious historians and sociologists of science to consider the social and economic components of what might first appear to have been problems within the strict domains of science.

Edgar Zilsel, the author of a well-known paper on the sociological roots of science,[5] has adopted a more moderate economic-deterministic position in his researches. He is convinced that the advent of early capitalistic society broke down the ancient barriers separating the scholar from the craftsman, the man of formal knowledge from the man of practical knowledge. From antiquity through the Middle Ages, the philosopher and the priest were socially superior to the metallurgist, potter, ship-builder, or other craftsman. The scholar excelled in logic, speculative thinking, and mathe-

---

[3] Letter to Heinz Starkenburg; London, Jan. 25, 1894.

[4] For a balanced assessment of Soviet scholarship in the history of science see David Joravsky, "Soviet Views on the History of Science," *Isis*, XLVI, no. 143 (1955). Joravsky's study of *Soviet Marxism and Natural Science, 1917–1932* (1961) is an indispensable guide to Hessen's ideological and philosophical milieu.

[5] Edgar Zilsel, "The Sociological Roots of Science," *The American Journal of Sociology*, XLVII, no. 4 (1942).

matics; the craftsman had a special knowledge of the material substances on earth. Theory and practice were thus separated for centuries until the needs of an emerging capitalistic society joined them together to produce modern science.

Zilsel's scholar-craftsman theory has had a wide influence. For example, the documentation in Crombie's and Baron's papers indicate that they have found it useful. However, it should be understood that these two are not offering a Marxist explanation for the rise of science in the West. It is possible to seek the economic and social roots of science without making a commitment to the Marxist philosophy of history. A case in point is the Islamic philosopher Ibn-Khaldun (1332–1406), who related the emergence of early science to the development of economic activity in the growing city and state.

At first glance there might seem to be little difference between Zilsel's search for the sociological roots of modern science and Robert K. Merton's sociological analysis of seventeenth-century English science and technology (p. 39). Merton has been placed in a separate category because the massive amount of statistical and historical data he used to support his cautiously drawn conclusions has made his paper one of the classic studies in the sociology of science. Furthermore, while Zilsel was satisfied with a socioeconomic interpretation, Merton added a new element — religion — to that interpretation. Merton's thesis that interacting socioeconomic and religious forces spurred on the growth of science in England was inspired by Boris Hessen and the great German sociologist Max Weber. Hessen supplied the hints for the technological sources of science and Merton undertook a study to determine the nature of the relationship between science and technology. His study exceeds Hessen's in thoroughness and objectivity and his modest conclusions have found wider acceptance than Hessen's exaggerated claims.

Max Weber's identification of the Protestant ethic with the rise of capitalism carries with it the implication that modern science and technology, two elements associated with modern capitalistic culture, may owe their recent rapid growth to the same source. Merton tested the validity of this implication by concentrating his study on England at a time when she had become one of the leaders of world science and concluded that Puritanism provided a system of values and beliefs which fostered the development of seventeenth-century English science.

It might appear that Merton weakened the force of his argument by focussing his attention upon the relationship between religion, science, and technology in England *alone*. However, by systematically studying one national culture he facilitated the acceptance of his conclusions. In place of sweeping, and unsupported, generalizations covering the whole scope of European science, we have a sociologist who has gathered and examined the existing, relevant data in the critical period of one society. Merton readily admits the possibility of multiple causation in history and he is aware that science flourished in pre-Reformation Italy without the stimulus of the Protestant ethic. However, whatever the causal connection may be in other societies and other eras, Merton feels he has revealed the source of seventeenth-century English scientific activity by linking together Puritanism, technology, and science.

Coupled with the Merton selection is a more recent example of relevant research in the sociology of science. Sociologist Joseph Ben-David (p. 47) asks a question that would not likely occur to a historian: How, and when, was the *role* of the modern scientist established in European society? In effect, this means he has shifted the focus from the emergence of modern science to the emergence of the role of the modern scientist. The larger question remains, of course, as to whether or not the intellectual basis of modern science must necessarily precede the creation of the social role of the modern scientist. Current thinking within the history of science would support the contention that the scientist's role emerged only after the ideas central to modern science had coalesced. But once again a sociologist's insight has opened new avenues of research for the historian.

The Weber-Mertonian position on Puritanism and science has been expanded by the researches of the Dutch historian of science Reijer Hooykaas (p. 55). Choosing examples from Continental as well as English scientists and theologians, Hooykaas came to the conclusion that the religious attitudes of ascetic Protestants generally furthered the development of science. Protestantism as the fertilizing agent of modern science has had many scholarly champions. Catholicism, on the defensive because of the celebrated but misunderstood Galileo incident, and still recovering from the effects of the belief that it had smothered medieval science, has had fewer scholars interested in determining its place in the rise of modern science. The question of the religious influences on the progress of science has not been resolved. The strongest case for the Catholic position is a list of the Catholic scientists who contributed to the sciences during the sixteenth and seventeenth centuries. Such a list has been compiled by Father François Russo, S.J. (p. 62) in the conclusion to an article he wrote in direct reply to Hooykaas.

The religious, and more specifically the Protestant, interpretation of the emergence of modern science has been severely criticized in Lewis S. Feuer's book on the psychological origins of modern science (p. 69). According to Weber and Merton, Calvinist theology aided the growth of science by its promise of salvation through labor in the world. The scientist, toiling to understand God's creation and help his fellow men, fulfilled the duties specified for him by Calvinistic doctrine. Salvation through scientific labor as the key to the birth of modern science is completely unacceptable to Feuer. He searched for an emotional basis of scientific activity and de-

cided that it was not a gloomy asceticism but a "hedonist-libertarian" spirit that produced the inquiring mind and stimulated science, and that the first modern scientists were philosophical optimists who contemplated the material universe in an inquisitive and joyful manner. They were driven by a spirit of play, not work — a spirit antagonistic to the repression and asceticism of the Christian faith. In short, a psychological revolution prepared the way for modern science.

Feuer is concerned not only with the rise of science in the West but also with the failure of other societies to foster scientific growth. Throughout his investigation, he made full use of the scholarly researches of historians of science but relied upon concepts derived from psychoanalysis — repression, Oedipus complex — to establish the theoretical basis of his argument. His free application of psychoanalytic concepts to the study of historical events has not been accepted by the majority of historians who question the validity of this technique. Nevertheless, Feuer provided a necessary corrective to the influential and better known religious interpretation of the origins of modern science.

The next group of selections are representative of two recent, and not completely formulated, attempts to find new sources for modern science. The union of Renaissance art and science, associated in the popular mind with the name of Leonardo da Vinci, is not a new theme in Renaissance studies. In the last decades of the nineteenth century, Leonardo was honored as a creative genius, a man with great artistic and engineering talents and the virtual founder of modern science. Duhem punctured this legend when he showed that Leonardo's scientific knowledge was largely borrowed from medieval thinkers. The medievalists removed Leonardo from his preeminent position, but there still remained the idea that Renaissance art was closely allied with the new sciences. In support of this view one could point to the artist's interest in architecture, engineering, the mathematical problems of perspective, and botanical and anatomical illustration. Art historians, notably Erwin Panofsky, have studied this alliance, but historians of science have tended to neglect it. This is not true of the Galilean authority Giorgio de Santillana. In a perceptive essay, de Santillana began what he calls "the tricky and . . . difficult" task of unraveling the influence of art on the nascent science of the fifteenth century (p. 76).

As one studies the science of earlier times, he must be careful not to judge the past in terms of twentieth-century developments. It is easy, and short-sighted, to concentrate solely on those aspects of scientific endeavor acceptable to the scientific community today. The historian knows that science gives us reliable, but not infallible, answers to our questions about the material universe. He knows that the "right" scientific explanations of one century might become the "wrong" explanations of the next. In searching for the origins of modern science, he must be willing to explore modes of thought that have been abandoned by twentieth-century scientists. This means that he must give serious consideration to magic, alchemy, and astrology, for modern science arose out of a matrix that included these occult sciences.

The study of the occult sciences has been hampered by individuals whose historical investigations are motivated by the belief that the alchemist or astrologer did indeed have the secret of the universe. Fortunately, these are in the minority, and others can be named — Lynn Thorndike and Walter Pagel, for example — whose researches into magic, alchemy, and astrology have earned them a high place among historians of science. No one has yet written a detailed interpretative study of occult thought and its role in the birth of modern science. Allen G. Debus, a specialist in Renaissance alchemy, has made an important contribution to that study with his investigation of alchemy and its relationship to early modern science (p. 82).

Many of the explanations for the rise of modern science reviewed here have been based on *external* causes. Social, economic, religious, psychological, and artistic forces — all of them external to the substance of science itself — have been advanced as the true stimuli of scientific progress. However, if one reads the works published by leading historians of science during the last twenty or thirty years, he will find that the *externalists* have lost their influence. They have been replaced by an *internalist* school, led by the late French historian of science, Professor Alexandre Koyré (p. 97), and strongly supported by his English spokesman, A. Rupert Hall (p. 89).

The internalists believe that scientific ideas have a life of their own — one that is insulated, as Hall wrote, from the "general cultural, economic, and social state of a nation or community of nations." The history of science, in the eyes of the internalists, is analogous to the history of philosophy or intellectual history. For them, it is no more meaningful to search for the economic and social roots of Newton's *Principia* than it is to seek the economic and social roots of Kant's *Critique of Pure Reason* or Whitehead's *Process and Reality*. Of course, science is created within a cultural, social, and economic setting that may exert an influence, but that setting does not determine the direction and rate of growth of scientific thought. This is determined by the interplay of ideas within science.

The internalists, or intellectualists, have found it somewhat easier to accept a connection between medieval and early modern science than many of the externalists. The notion of a flow of ideas from the thirteenth to the seventeenth century is plausible to those who stress the intellectual foundations of science. But although they admit the indebtedness of modern to medieval science, the internalists are not prepared to equate the two. They still speak of the radical changes in science brought about during the sixteenth and seventeenth centuries. How is one to account for these discontinuities — these radical changes? The internalists reply that the causes for the changes come from within science and can be viewed as part of the struggle between novelty, tradition, alteration, and evolution that characterize the emergence of revolutionary ideas in any intellectual enterprise.

The internalists have been given the last word because their interpretation of the rise of modern science is acceptable to most historians of science today. Perhaps some future proponents of an externalist interpretation will offer strong proof that the intellect is decisively conditioned by external forces. However, in order to do so, they must accomplish what none of their predecessors have hitherto done. They must thoroughly acquaint themselves with the scholarship produced by the internalists and then create a carefully documented alternative to the internalist position. Until that is accomplished, the origin and conceptual growth of science will be best studied as a part of man's intellectual heritage.

[NOTE ON TERMS: I have deliberately avoided the term "Scientific Revolution" and used the less elegant, but more precise, phrase, "the rise of science in the sixteenth and seventeenth centuries." The "Scientific Revolution" can refer to at least three different historical periods: *a.* it is sometimes limited to a designation of the heightened scientific activity of the seventeenth century; *b.* it has been used to characterize all of the developments in science between 1500 and 1800; *c.* recently, it has been used in reference to the great changes occurring in science since 1940. The reader will find that our authors will be using the term in senses *a.* and *b.* EDITOR'S NOTE.]

The Conflict of Opinion

The traditional explanation stressed the sterility of the Middle Ages and the sudden appearance of modern science in the Renaissance:

> "We have now to consider more especially a long and barren period, which intervened between the scientific activity of ancient Greece and that of modern Europe; and which we may, therefore, call the Stationary Period of Science. . . ."
>
> — WILLIAM WHEWELL

To which the medievalists replied:

> "The mechanical and physical science of which modern times are justly proud unfolds, through an uninterrupted series of barely perceptible improvements, from the doctrines taught in the medieval schools."
>
> — PIERRE DUHEM

And the Renaissance scholars countered:

> "When Duhem, the arch-opponent of Burckhardt, reached a vantage point from which he could look back over his beloved fourteenth century and forward to the sixteenth and seventeenth centuries, to all intents and purposes he withdrew his objections to Burckhardt's thesis of a renaissance in science and gave it his valuable, though grudging, support."
>
> — EDWARD ROSEN

Various explanations were offered to account for the rise of modern science in the sixteenth and seventeeth centuries:

> "Science flourished step by step with the development and flourishing of the bourgeoisie."
>
> — BORIS M. HESSEN

> "A number of studies have shown that the Protestant ethos exerted a stimulative effect upon capitalism. Since science and technology play such dominant rôles in modern capitalistic culture, it is possible that tangible relationship likewise exist between the development of science and Puritanism."
>
> — ROBERT K. MERTON

> "Ancient science failed to develop not because of its immanent shortcomings but because those who did scientific work did not see themselves, nor were they seen by others, as scientists, but primarily as philosophers, medical practitioners, or astrologers. . . ."
>
> — JOSEPH BEN-DAVID

"The scientist of the seventeenth century was a philosophical optimist; delight and joy in man's status pervaded his theory of knowledge and of the universe. And it was this revolution in man's emotions which was the basis for the change in his ideas."

— LEWIS S. FEUER

". . . this investigation seems to suggest that two of the major features of the Scientific Renaissance, namely, the change-over from Form to Function, and the rise of a 'natural law' unconnected with the affairs of human society, have their origin in a specific transformation of the arts. . . ."

— GIORGIO DE SANTILLANA

"One cannot deny that a careful analysis of the alchemical texts, the pharmaceutical works and the metallurgical treatises of the Renaissance for their actual chemical content is of profound importance for our knowledge of the growth of science as we know it, but the blanket dismissal of other supposedly 'non-scientific' aspects of early chemistry to the realm of occultism, mysticism and magical hocus-pocus does nothing to add to our knowledge of the birth of modern science."

— ALLEN G. DEBUS

But all explanations based on external factors have been challenged by the internalists:

"Clearly, externalist explanations of the history of science have lost their interest as well as their interpretative capacity. One reason for this may be that such explanations tell us very little about science itself . . . Social and economic relations are rather concerned with the scientific movement than with science as a system of knowledge of nature (theoretical and practical); they help us to understand the public face of science and the public reaction to scientists; to evaluate the propaganda that scientists distribute about themselves, and occasionally — but only occasionally — to see why the subject of scientific discussion takes a new turn."

— A. RUPERT HALL

PHYSICAL SCIENCE IN
THE MIDDLE AGES

WILLIAM WHEWELL

"Science was his forte and omniscience his foible," wrote the wit Sydney Smith of the Reverend William Whewell (1794–1866), Master of Trinity College, Cambridge. An influential figure in the development of English science in the nineteenth century, Whewell was at once a divine, mineralogist, philosopher, and historian of science. His pioneering work in the history of science—*History of the Inductive Sciences*, 3 vols. (1837)—grew out of his attempt to reform philosophy by investigating the actual methods utilized by the men who had revealed the great scientific truths pertaining to the physical universe. Modern research in the history of science has gone far beyond Whewell's volumes, but throughout Victorian England they were rightly considered as classics in their field.

Among his many talents was an ability to coin scientific neologisms. It was Whewell who added *scientist* and *physicist* to the English language, as well as *ion, cathode, anode, eocene,* and other technical terms.

WE HAVE NOW TO CONSIDER . . . a long and barren period, which intervened between the scientific activity of ancient Greece and that of modern Europe; and which we may, therefore, call the Stationary Period of Science. It would be to no purpose to enumerate the various forms in which, during these times, men reproduced the discoveries of the inventive ages; or to trace in them the small successes of Art, void of any principle of genuine Philosophy. Our object requires rather that we should point out the general and distinguishing features of the intellect and habits of those times. We must endeavor to delineate the character of the Stationary Period, and, as far as possible, to analyze its defects and errors; and thus obtain some knowledge of the causes of its barrenness and darkness.

. . . Real scientific progress requires distinct general Ideas, applied to many special and certain Facts. In the period of which we now have to speak, men's Ideas were obscured; their disposition to bring their general views into accordance with Facts was enfeebled. They were thus led to employ themselves unprofitably, among indistinct and unreal notions. And the evil of these tendencies was further inflamed by moral peculiarities in the character of those times; — by an abjectness of thought on the one hand, which could not help looking towards some intellectual superior, and by an impatience of dissent on the other. To this must be added an enthusiastic temper, which, when introduced into speculation, tends to subject the mind's operations to ideas altogether distorted and delusive.

These characteristics of the stationary period, its obscurity of thought, its servility, its intolerant disposition, and its enthusiastic temper, will be treated of in the four following chapters, on the Indistinctness of Ideas, the Commentatorial Spirit, the Dogmatism, and the Mysticism of the Middle Ages.

From William Whewell, *History of the Inductive Sciences* (New York, 1884), 3rd ed., Vol. I, pp. 185–251.

1

I. ON THE INDISTINCTNESS OF IDEAS OF
THE MIDDLE AGES

Collections of Opinions

The fact, that mere Collections of the opinions of physical philosophers came to hold a prominent place in literature, already indicated a tendency to an indistinct and wandering apprehension of such opinions. I speak of such works as Plutarch's five Books "on the Opinions of Philosophers," or the physical opinions which Diogenes Laërtius gives in his "Lives of the Philosophers." At an earlier period still, books of this kind appear; as for instance, a large portion of Pliny's Natural History, a work which has very appropriately been called the Encyclopædia of Antiquity; even Aristotle himself is much in the habit of enumerating the opinions of those who had preceded him. To present such statements as an important part of physical philosophy, shows an erroneous and loose apprehension of its nature. . . .

We may, therefore, consider the prevalence of Collections of the kind just referred to, as indicating a deficiency of philosophical talent in the ages now under review. As evidence of the same character, we may add the long train of publishers of Abstracts, Epitomes, Bibliographical Notices, and similar writers. All such writers are worthless for all purposes of *science,* and their labors may be considered as dead works; they have in them no principle of philosophical vitality; they draw their origin and nutriment from the death of true physical knowledge; and resemble the swarms of insects that are born from the perishing carcass of some noble animal.

Indistinctness of Ideas in Mechanics

But the indistinctness of thought which is so fatal a feature in the intellect of the stationary period, may be traced more directly in the works, even of the best authors, of those times. We find that they did not retain steadily the ideas on which the scientific success of the previous period had depended. For instance, it is a remarkable circumstance in the history of the science of Mechanics, that it did not make any advance from the time of Archimedes to that of Stevinus and Galileo. Archimedes had established the doctrine of the lever; several persons tried, in the intermediate time, to prove the property of the inclined plane, and none of them succeeded. . . .

Indistinctness of Ideas in Astronomy

. . . [I]t may be supposed, at first sight, that, with regard to astronomy, we have not the same ground for charging the stationary period with indistinctness of ideas on that subject, since they were able to acquire and verify, and, in some measure, to apply, the doctrines previously established. And, undoubtedly, it must be confessed that men's notions of the relations of space and number are never very indistinct. It appears to be impossible for these chains of elementary perception ever to be much entangled. The later Greeks, the Arabians, and the earliest modern astronomers, must have conceived the hypotheses of the Ptolemaic system with tolerable completeness. And yet, we may assert, that during the stationary period, men did not possess the notions, even of space and number, in that vivid and vigorous manner which enables them to discover new truths. . . .

Neglect of Physical Reasoning
in Christendom

If the Arabians, who, during the ages of which we are speaking, were the most eminent cultivators of science, entertained only such comparatively feeble and servile notions of its doctrines, it will easily be supposed, that in the Christendom of that period, where physical knowledge was comparatively neglected, there was still less distinctness and vividness in the prevalent ideas on such subjects. Indeed, during a considerable period of the history of the Christian Church, and by many of its principal authorities, the study of natural philosophy was not only disregarded but discommended. The great practical doctrines which were presented to men's minds, and the serious tasks, of the regulation of the will and affections, which religion impressed upon them, made inquiries of mere curiosity seem to be a reprehensible misapplication of human powers; and many of the fathers of the Church revived, in a still more peremptory form, the opinion of Socrates, that the only valuable philosophy is that which teaches us our moral duties and religious hopes. Thus Eusebius says, "It is not through ignorance of the things admired by them, but through contempt of their useless labor, that we think little of these matters, turning our souls to the exercise of better things.". . .

Intellectual Condition of the Religious Orders

. . . "And here," says the French historian of mathematics, whom I have followed . . . , "it is impossible not to reflect that all those men who, if they did not augment the treasure of the sciences, at least served to transmit it, were monks, or had been such originally. Convents were, during these stormy ages, the asylum of sciences and letters. Without these religious men, who, in the silence of their monasteries, occupied themselves in transcribing, in studying, and in imitating the works of the ancients, well or ill, those works would have perished; perhaps not one of them would have come down to us. The thread which connects us with the Greeks and Romans would have been snapt asunder; the precious productions of ancient literature would no more exist for us, than the works, if any there were, published before the catastrophe that annihilated that highly scientific nation, which, according to Bailly, existed in remote ages in the centre of Tartary, or at the roots of Caucasus. In the sciences we should have had all to create; and at the moment when the human mind should have emerged from its stupor and shaken off its slumbers, we should have been no more advanced than the Greeks were after the taking of Troy." He adds, that this consideration inspires feelings towards the religious orders very different

from those which, when he wrote, were prevalent among his countrymen. . . .

Popular Opinions

That, even in the best intellects, something was wanting to fit them for scientific progress and discovery, is obvious from the fact that science was so long absolutely stationary. And I have endeavored to show that one part of this deficiency was the want of the requisite clearness and vigor of the fundamental scientific ideas. If these were wanting, even in the most powerful and most cultivated minds, we may easily conceive that still greater confusion and obscurity prevailed in the common class of mankind. . . .

II. THE COMMENTATORIAL SPIRIT OF THE MIDDLE AGES

We have already noticed, that, after the first great achievements of the founders of sound speculation, in the different departments of human knowledge, had attracted the interest and admiration which those who became acquainted with them could not but give to them, there appeared a disposition among men to lean on the authority of some of these teachers; — to study the opinions of others as the only mode of forming their own; — to read nature through books; — to attend to what had been already thought and said, rather than to what really is and happens. This tendency of men's minds requires our particular consideration. Its manifestations were very important, and highly characteristic of the stationary period; it gave, in a great degree, a peculiar bias and direction to the intellectual activity of many centuries; and the kind of labor with which speculative men were occupied in consequence of this bias, took the place of that examination of realities which must be their employment, in order that real knowledge may make any decided progress. . . .

Natural Bias to Authority

It is very evident that, in such a bias of men's studies, there is something very natural; however strained and technical this erudition may have been, the propensities on which it depends are very general, and are easily seen. Deference to the authority of thoughtful and sagacious men, a disposition which men in general neither reject nor think they ought to reject in practical matters, naturally clings to them, even in speculation. It is a satisfaction to us to suppose that there are, or have been, minds of transcendent powers, of wide and wise views, superior to the common errors and blindness of our nature. . . .

Character of Commentators

The spirit of commentation, as has already been suggested, turns to questions of taste, of metaphysics, or morals, with far more avidity than to physics. Accordingly, critics and grammarians were peculiarly the growth of this school; and, though the commentators sometimes chose works of mathematical or physical science for their subject (as Proclus, who commented on Euclid's Geometry, and Simplicius, on Aristotle's Physics), these commentaries were, in fact, rather metaphysical than mathematical. It does not appear that the commentators have, in any instance, illustrated the author by bringing his assertions of facts to the test of experiment. . . .

The Commentator's professed object is to explain, to enforce, to illustrate doctrines assumed as true. He endeavors to adapt the work on which he employs himself to the state of information and of opinion in his own time; to elucidate obscurities and technicalities; to supply steps omitted in the reasoning; but he does not seek to obtain additional truths or new generalizations. He undertakes only to give what is virtually contained in his author; to develop, but not to create. He is a cultivator of the thoughts of others: his labor is not spent on a field of his own; he ploughs but to enrich the granary of another man. Thus he does not work as a freeman, but as one in a servile condition; or rather, his is a menial, and not a productive service: his office is to adorn the appearance of his master, not to increase his wealth.

III. OF THE MYSTICISM OF THE MIDDLE AGES

It has been already several times hinted, that a new and peculiar element was introduced into the Greek philosophy which occupied the attention of the Alexandrian school; and that this element tinged a large portion of the speculations of succeeding ages. We may speak of this peculiar element as *Mysticism;* for, from the notion usually conveyed by this term, the reader will easily apprehend the general character of the tendency now spoken of; and especially when he sees its effect pointed out in various subjects. Thus, instead of referring the events of the external world to space and time, to sensible connection and causation, men attempted to reduce such occurrences under spiritual and supersensual relations and dependencies; they referred them to superior intelligences, to theological conditions, to past and future events in the moral world, to states of mind and feelings, to the creatures of an imaginary mythology or demonology. And thus their physical Science became Magic, their Astronomy became Astrology, the study of the Composition of bodies became Alchemy, Mathematics became the contemplation of the Spiritual Relations of number and figure, and Philosophy became Theosophy. . . .

V. PROGRESS OF THE ARTS IN THE MIDDLE AGES

. . . The accusation of injustice towards the state of science in the middle ages, if we were to terminate our survey of them with what has hitherto been said, might be urged from obvious topics. How do we recognize, it might be asked, in a picture of mere confusion and mysticism of thought, of servility and dogmatism of character, the powers and acquirements to which we owe so many of the most important inventions which we now enjoy? Parchment and paper, printing and engraving, improved glass and steel, gunpowder, clocks, telescopes, the mariner's compass, the reformed calendar, the decimal notation, algebra, trigonometry, chemistry, counterpoint, an invention equivalent to a new creation of music; — these are all possessions which we inherit from that which has been so disparagingly termed the Stationary Period. Above all, let us look at the monuments of architecture of this period; — the admiration and the despair of modern architects, not only for their beauty, but for the skill disclosed in their construction. With all these evidences before us, how can we avoid allowing that the masters of the middle ages not only made some small progress in Astronomy, which has, grudgingly as it would seem, been admitted in a former Book; but also that they were no small proficients in other sciences, in Optics, in Harmonics, in Physics, and, above all, in Mechanics?

If, it may be added, we are allowed, in the present day, to refer to the perfection of our arts as evidence of the advanced state of our physical philosophy; — if our steam-engines, our gas-illumination, our buildings, our navigation, our manufactures, are cited as triumphs of science; — shall not prior inventions, made under far heavier disadvantages, — shall not greater works, produced in an earlier state of knowledge, also be admitted as witnesses that the middle ages had their share, and that not a small or doubtful one, of science?

To these questions I answer, by distinguishing between Art, and Science in that sense of general Inductive Systematic Truth, which it bears in this work. To separate and compare, with precision, these two processes, belongs to the Philosophy of Induction; and the attempt must be reserved for another place: but the leading differences are sufficiently obvious. Art is practical, Science is speculative: the former is seen in doing; the latter rests in the contemplation of what is known. The art of the builder appears in his edifice, though he may never have meditated on the abstract propositions on which its stability and strength depends. The Science of the mathematical mechanician consists in his seeing that, under certain conditions, bodies must sustain each other's pressure, though he may never have applied his knowledge in a single case.

Now the remark which I have to make is this: — in all cases the Arts are prior to the related Sciences. Art is the parent, not the progeny, of Science; the realization of principles in practice forms part of the prelude, as well as of the sequel, of theoretical discovery. And thus the inventions of the middle ages, which have been above enumerated, though at the present day they may be portions of our sciences, are no evidence that the sciences then existed; but only that those powers of practical observation and practical skill were at work, which prepare the way for theoretical views and scientific discoveries. . . .

Architecture of the Middle Ages

But though we are thus compelled to disallow several of the claims which have been put forward in support of the scientific character of the middle ages, there are two points in which we may, I conceive, really trace the progress of scientific ideas among them; and which, therefore, may be considered as the prelude to the period of discovery. I mean their practical architecture, and their architectural treatises.

In a previous chapter of this book, we have endeavored to explain how the indistinctness of ideas, which attended the decline of the Roman empire, appears in the forms of their architecture; — in the disregard, which the decorative construction exhibits, of the necessary mechanical conditions of support. . . .

When, after this deep decline, architecture rose again, as it did in the twelfth and succeeding centuries, in the exquisitely beautiful and skilful forms of the Gothic style, what was the nature of the change which had taken place, so far as it bears upon the progress of science? It was this: — the idea of true mechanical relations in an edifice had been revived in men's minds, as far as was requisite for the purposes of art and beauty: and this, though a very different thing from the possession of the idea as an element of speculative science, was the proper preparation for that acquisition. . . .

Treatises on Architecture

. . . The earliest treatises on Architecture come before us under the form which the commentatorial spirit of the middle ages inspired. They are Translations of Vitruvius, with Annotations. In some of these, particularly that of Cesare Cesariano, published at Como, in 1521, we see, in a very curious manner, how the habit of assuming that, in every department of literature, the ancients must needs be their masters, led these writers to subordinate the members of their own architecture to the precepts of the Roman author. . . . But independently of this, we find, in the best works of the architects of all ages (including engineers), evidence that the true idea of mechanical pressure exists among them more distinctly than among men in general, although it may not be developed in a scientific form. This is true up to our own time, and the arts which such persons cultivate could not be successfully exercised if it were not so. Hence the writings of architects and engineers during the middle ages do really form a prelude to the works on scientific mechanics. Vitruvius, in his *Architecture*, and Julius Frontinus, who, under Vespasian, wrote *On Aqueducts*, of which he was superintendent, have transmitted to us the principal part of what we know respecting the practical mechanics and hydraulics of the Romans. In modern times the series is resumed. The early writers on architecture are also writers on engineering, and often on hydrostatics: for example, Leonardo da Vinci wrote on the equilibrium of water. And thus we are led up to Stevinus of Bruges, who was engineer to Prince Maurice of Nassau, and inspector of the dykes in Holland; and in whose work, on the processes of his art, is contained the first clear modern statement of the scientific principles of hydrostatics.

THE DISCOVERY OF THE WORLD
AND OF MAN

JAKOB C. BURCKHARDT

When the Swiss historian Jakob C. Burckhardt (1818–1897) wrote *The Civilization of the Renaissance in Italy* (1860) and laid the basis for future study of the Renaissance, there was little interest in the historical examination of the development of science. William Whewell's *History of the Inductive Sciences*, although translated into German in the 1840's, was not widely known or used on the Continent. Burckhardt's synthesis, therefore, took little notice of Renaissance science but it perpetuated the view that the emergnce of modern science was an outcome of Renaissance man's new awareness of the natural world.

JOURNEYS OF THE ITALIANS

FREED FROM THE COUNTLESS BONDS which elsewhere in Europe checked progress, having reached a high degree of individual development and been schooled by the teachings of antiquity, the Italian mind now turned to the discovery of the outward universe, and to the representation of it in speech and in form.

On the journeys of the Italians to distant parts of the world, we can here make but a few general observations. The crusades had opened unknown distances to the European mind, and awakened in all the passion for travel and adventure. It may be hard to indicate precisely the point where this passion allied itself with, or became the servant of, the thirst for knowledge; but it was in Italy that this was first and most completely the case. Even in the crusades the interest of the Italians was wider than that of other nations, since they already were a naval power and had commercial relations wi*h the East. From time immemorial the Me²iterranean sea had given to the nations that dwelt on its shores mental impulses different from those which governed the peoples of the North; and never, from the very structure of their character, could the Italians be adventurers in the sense which the word bore among the Teutons. After they were once at home in all the eastern harbours of the Mediterranean, it was natural that the most enterprising among them should be led to join that vast international movement of the Mohammedans which there found its outlet. A new half of the world lay, as it were, freshly discovered before them. Or, like Polo of Venice, they were caught in the current of the Mongolian peoples, and carried on to the steps of the throne of the Great Khan. At an early period, we find Italians sharing in the discoveries made in the Atlantic ocean; it was the Genoese who, in the thirteenth century, found the Canary Islands. In the same year, 1291, when Ptolemais, the last remnant of the Christian East, was lost, it was again the Genoese who made the first known attempt to find a sea-passage to the East Indies. Columbus himself is but the greatest of a long list of Italians who, in the service of the western nations, sailed into distant seas. The true discoverer, however, is not the man who first chances to stumble upon anything, but the man who finds what

From Jakob Burckhardt, *The Civilization of the Period of the Renaissance in Italy*, tr. S. G. C. Middlemore (London, 1878), Vol. II, pp. 3–20.

he has sought. Such a one alone stands in a link with the thoughts and interests of his predecessors, and this relationship will also determine the account he gives of his search. For which reason the Italians, although their claim to be the first comers on this or that shore may be disputed, will yet retain their title to be pre-eminently the nation of discoverers for the whole latter part of the Middle Ages. The fuller proof of this assertion belongs to the special history of discoveries. Yet ever and again we turn with admiration to the august figure of the great Genoese, by whom a new continent beyond the ocean was demanded, sought, and found; and who was the first to be able to say: "il mondo è poco" — the world is not so large as men have thought. At the time when Spain gave Alexander VI to the Italians, Italy gave Columbus to the Spaniards. Only a few weeks before the death of that pope (July 7th, 1503), Columbus wrote from Jamaica his noble letter to the thankless Catholic kings, which the ages to come can never read without profound emotion. In a codicil to his will, dated Valladolid, May 4th, 1506, he bequeathed to "his beloved home, the Republic of Genoa, the prayer-book which Pope Alexander had given him, and which in prison, in conflict, and in every kind of adversity had been to him the greatest of comforts." It seems as if these words cast upon the abhorred name of Borgia one last gleam of grace and mercy.

The development of geographical and the allied sciences among the Italians must, like the history of their voyages, be touched upon but very briefly. A superficial comparison of their achievements with those of other nations shows an early and striking superiority on their part. Where, in the middle of the fifteenth century, could be found, anywhere but in Italy, such a union of geographical, statistical, and historical knowledge as was found in Aeneas Sylvius? Not only in his great geographical work, but in his letters and commentaries, he describes with equal mastery landscapes, cities, manners, industries and products, political conditions and constitutions, wherever he can use his own observation or the evidence of eye-witnesses. What he takes from books is naturally of less moment. Even the short sketch of that valley in the Tyrolese Alps, where Frederick III had given him a benefice, and still more his description of Scotland, leaves untouched none of the relations of human life, and displays a power and method of unbiased observation and comparison impossible in any but a countryman of Columbus, trained in the school of the ancients. Thousands saw and, in part, knew what he did, but they felt no impulse to draw a picture of it, and were unconscious that the world desired such pictures.

In geography as in other matters, it is vain to attempt to distinguish how much is to be attributed to the study of the ancients, and how much to the special genius of the Italians. They saw and treated the things of this world from an objective point of view, even before they were familiar with the ancient literature, partly because they were themselves a half-ancient people, and partly because their political circumstances predisposed them to it; but they would not so rapidly have attained to such perfection had not the old geographers showed them the way. The influence of the existing Italian geographies on the spirit and tendencies of the travellers and discoverers was also inestimable. Even the simple "dilettante" of a science — if in the present case we should assign to Aeneas Sylvius so low a rank — can diffuse just that sort of general interest in the subject which prepares for new pioneers the indispensable groundwork of a favorable predisposition in the public mind. True discoverers in any science know well what they owe to such mediation.

NATURAL SCIENCE IN ITALY

For the position of the Italians in the sphere of the natural sciences, we must refer the reader to the special treatises on the subject, of which the only one with which we are familiar is the superficial and depreciatory work of Libri. The dispute as to the priority of particular discoveries concerns us all the less, since we hold that, at any time, and among any civilized people, a man may appear who, starting with very scanty preparation, is driven by an irresistible impulse into the path of scientific investigation, and through his native gifts achieves the most astonishing success. Such men were Gerbert of Rheims and Roger Bacon. That they were masters of the whole knowledge of the age in their several departments was a natural consequence of the spirit in which they worked. When once the veil of illusion was torn asunder, when once the dread of nature and the slavery to books and tradition were overcome, countless problems lay before them for solution. It is another matter when a whole people takes a natural delight in the study and investigation of nature, at a time when other nations are indifferent, that is to say, when the discoverer is not threatened or wholly ignored, but can count on the friendly support of congenial spirits. That this was the case in Italy, is unquestionable. The Italian students of nature trace with pride in the "Divine Comedy" the hints and proofs of Dante's scientific interest in nature. On his claim to priority in this or that discovery or reference, we must leave the men of science to decide; but every layman must be struck by the wealth of his observations on the external world, shown merely in his pictures and comparisons. He, more than any other modern poet, takes them from reality, whether in nature or human life, and uses them, never as mere ornament, but in order to give the reader the fullest and most adequate sense of his meaning. It is in astronomy that he appears chiefly as a scientific specialist, though it must not be forgotten that many astronomical allusions in his great poem, which now appear to us learned, must then have been intelligible to the general reader. Dante, learning apart, appeals to a popular knowledge of the heavens, which the Italians of his day, from the mere fact that they were nautical people, had in common with

the ancients. This knowledge of the rising and setting of the constellations has been rendered superfluous to the modern world by calendars and clocks, and with it has gone whatever interest in astronomy the people may once have had. Nowadays, with our schools and handbooks, every child knows — what Dante did not know — that the earth moves round the sun; but the interest once taken in the subject itself has given place, except in the case of astronomical specialists, to the most absolute indifference.

The pseudo-science, which also dealt with the stars, proves nothing against the inductive spirit of the Italians of that day. That spirit was but crossed, and at times overcome, by the passionate desire to penetrate the future. We shall recur to the subject of astrology when we come to speak of the moral and religious character of the people.

The Church treated this and other pseudo-sciences nearly always with toleration; and showed itself actually hostile even to genuine science only when a charge of heresy together with necromancy was also in question — which certainly was often the case. A point which it would be interesting to decide is this: whether, and in what cases, the Dominican (and also the Franciscan) Inquisitors in Italy were conscious of the falsehood of the charges, and yet condemned the accused, either to oblige some enemy of the prisoner or from hatred to natural science, and particularly to experiments. The latter doubtless occurred, but it is not easy to prove the fact. What helped to cause such persecutions in the North, namely, the opposition made to the innovators by the upholders of the received official, scholastic system of nature, was of little or no weight in Italy. Pietro of Abano, at the beginning of the fourteenth century, is well known to have fallen a victim to the envy of another physician, who accused him before the Inquisition of heresy and magic; and something of the same kind may have happened in the case of his Paduan contemporary, Giovannino

Sanguinacci, who was known as an innovator in medical practice. He escaped, however, with banishment. Nor must it be forgotten that the inquisitorial power of the Dominicans was exercised less uniformly in Italy than in the North. Tyrants and free cities in the fourteenth century treated the clergy at times with such sovereign contempt, that very different matters from natural science went unpunished. But when, with the fifteenth century, antiquity became the leading power in Italy, the breach it made in the old system was turned to account by every branch of secular science. Humanism, nevertheless, attracted to itself the best strength of the nation, and thereby, no doubt, did injury to the inductive investigation of nature. Here and there the Inquisition suddenly started into life, and punished or burned physicians as blasphemers or magicians. In such cases it is hard to discover what was the true motive underlying the condemnation. And after all, Italy, at the close of the fifteenth century, with Paolo Toscanelli, Luca Pacciolo and Leonardo da Vinci, held incomparably the highest place among European nations in mathematics and the natural sciences, and the learned men of every country, even Regiomontanus and Copernicus, confessed themselves its pupils.

A significant proof of the wide-spread interest in natural history is found in the zeal which showed itself at an early period for the collection and comparative study of plants and animals. Italy claims to be the first creator of botanical gardens, though possibly they may have served a chiefly practical end, and the claim to priority may be itself disputed. It is of far greater importance that princes and wealthy men in laying out their pleasure-gardens, instinctively made a point of collecting the greatest possible number of different plants in all their species and varieties. Thus in the fifteenth century the noble grounds of the Medicean Villa Careggi appear from the descriptions we have of them to have been almost a botanical garden, with countless specimens of different trees and shrubs. Of the same kind was a villa of the Cardinal Trivulzio, at the beginning of the sixteenth century, in the Roman Campagna towards Tivoli, with hedges made up of various species of roses, with trees of every description — the fruit-trees especially showing an astonishing variety — with twenty different sorts of vines and a large kitchen-garden. This is evidently something very different from the score or two of familiar medicinal plants, which were to be found in the garden of any castle or monastery in Western Europe. Along with a careful cultivation of fruit for the purposes of the table, we find an interest in the plant for its own sake, on account of the pleasure it gives to the eye. We learn from the history of art at how late a period this passion for botanical collections was laid aside, and gave place to what was considered the picturesque style of landscape-gardening.

The collections, too, of foreign animals not only gratified curiosity, but served also the higher purposes of observation. The facility of transport from the southern and eastern harbours of the Mediterranean, and the mildness of the Italian climate, made it practicable to buy the largest animals of the south, or to accept them as presents from the Sultans. The cities and princes were especially anxious to keep live lions, even when the lion was not, as in Florence, the emblem of the State. The lions' den was generally in or near the government palace, as in Perugia and Florence; in Rome, it lay on the slope of the Capitol. The beasts sometimes served as executioners of political judgments, and no doubt, apart from this, they kept alive a certain terror in the popular mind. Their condition was also held to be ominous of good or evil. Their fertility, especially, was considered a sign of public prosperity, and no less a man than Giovanni Villani thought it worth recording that he was present at the delivery of a lioness. The cubs were often given to allied states and princes, or to Condottieri, as a reward of valor. In addition to the lions, the Florentine began very early to keep leopards, for which a special keeper was appointed. Borso of Ferrara used to set his lions to fight with bulls, bears, and wild boars.

By the end of the fifteenth century, however, true menageries (serragli), now reckoned part of the suitable appointments of a court, were kept by many of the princes. "It belongs to the position of the great," says Matarazzo, "to keep horses, dogs, mules, falcons, and other birds, court-jesters, singers, and foreign animals." The menageries at Naples, in the time of Ferrante and others, contained a giraffe and a zebra, presented, it seems, by the ruler of Baghdad. Filippo Maria Visconti possessed not only horses which cost him each 500 or 1,000 pieces of gold, and valuable English dogs, but a number of leopards brought from all parts of the East; the expense of his hunting-birds which were collected from the countries of Northern Europe, amounted to 3,000 pieces of gold a month. "The Cremonese say that the Emperor Frederick II brought an elephant into their city, sent him from India by Prester John," we read in Brunetto Latini; Petrarch records the dying out of the elephants in Italy. King Emanuel the Great of Portugal knew well what he was about when he presented Leo X with an elephant and a rhinoceros. It was under such circumstances that the foundations of a scientific zoology and botany were laid.

A practical fruit of these zoological studies was the establishment of studs, of which the Mantuan, under Francesco Gonzaga, was esteemed the first in Europe. An interest in, and knowledge of the different breeds of horses is as old, no doubt, as riding itself, and the crossing of the European with the Asiatic must have been common from the time of the crusades. In Italy, a special inducement to perfect the breed was offered by the prizes at the horse-races held in every considerable town in the peninsula. In the Mantuan stables were found the infallible winners in these contests, as well as the best military chargers, and the horses best suited by their stately appearance for presents to great people. Gonzaga kept stallions and mares from Spain, Ireland, Africa, Thrace, and Cilicia, and for the sake of the last he cultivated the friendship of the Sultan. All possible experiments were here tried, in order to produce the most perfect animals.

Even human menageries were not wanting. The famous Cardinal Ippolito Medici, bastard of Giuliano, Duke of Nemours, kept at his strange court a troop of barbarians who talked no less than twenty different languages, and who were all of them perfect specimens of their races. Among them were incomparable *voltigeurs* of the best blood of the North African Moors, Tartar bowmen, Negro wrestlers, Indian divers, and Turks, who generally accompanied the Cardinal on his hunting expeditions. When he was overtaken by an early death (1535), this motley band carried the corpse on their shoulders from Itri to Rome, and mingled with the general mourning for the open-handed Cardinal their medley of tongues and violent gesticulations.

These scattered notices of the relations of the Italians to natural science, and their interest in the wealth and variety of the products of nature, are only fragments of a great subject. No one is more conscious than the author of the defects in his knowledge on this point. Of the multitude of special works in which the subject is adequately treated, even the names are but imperfectly known to him. . . .

THE CONTINUITY OF MEDIEVAL AND 17th CENTURY SCIENCE

ALISTAIR C. CROMBIE

A native Australian, holding science degrees from the Universities of Melbourne and Cambridge, Alistair C. Crombie (1915–) is currently Senior Lecturer in the History of Science at Oxford University. Crombie's main contribution to our understanding of medieval science was made in 1953 with his publication of *Robert Grosseteste and the Origins of Experimental Science: 1100–1700.* Here he claimed that the logical structure, and to some extent the practice, of experimental science can be traced to the Middle Ages. A year prior to this work, he issued the first comprehensive history of medieval science in the English language: *Medieval and Early Modern Science* (rev. ed., 1959). Medieval science, for Crombie, includes both the physical and biological sciences and it is seen in relation to philosophy, technology, and the arts.

MANY SCHOLARS NOW AGREE that 15th-century humanism, which arose in Italy and spread northwards, was an interruption in the development of science. The "revival of letters" deflected interest from matter to literary style and, in turning back to classical antiquity, its devotees affected to ignore the scientific progress of the previous three centuries. The same absurd conceit that led the humanists to abuse and misrepresent their immediate predecessors for using Latin constructions unknown to Cicero and to put out the propaganda which, in varying degrees, has captivated historical opinion until quite recently, also allowed them to borrow from the scholastics without acknowledgment. This habit affected almost all the great scientists of the 16th and 17th centuries, whether Catholic or Protestant, and it has required the labours of a Duhem or a Thorndike or a Maier to show that their statements on matters of history cannot be accepted at their face value.

This literary movement performed some important services for science. Ultimately perhaps the greatest of these was the simplification and clarification of language, although this occurred mainly in the 17th century when it applied particularly to French, but also, under the influence of the Royal Society, to English. The most immediate service was to supply the means of developing mathematical technique. The development and physical application of the many problems discussed in Oxford, Paris, Heidelberg or Padua in terms of logic and simple geometry were sharply limited by lack of mathematics. It was unusual for medieval university students to progress beyond the first book of Euclid, and although the Hindu system was known, Roman numerals continued in use, although not among mathematicians, into the 17th century. Competent mathematicians, such as Fibonacci, Jordanus Nemorarius, Bradwardine, Orseme, Richard of Wallingford and Regiomontanus were, of course, better equipped and made original contributions to geometry, algebra and trigonometry, but there was no continuous mathematical tradition comparable with that in logic. The new translations by the humanists, presented to the public through the newly-invented printing press, placed the wealth of Greek mathematics within easy grasp. Some of these Greek authors, such as Euclid and Ptolemy, had been studied in the preceding centuries; others, such as Archimedes, Apollonius and Diophantus, were available in earlier translations but not generally studied. Among works on applied mathematics Ptolemy's *Cosmographia* and *Geographia* were both printed several times, but the *Almagest* was not printed, except as epitomised by Regiomontanus, until early in the 16th century. Few Arabic astronomical writings were printed. By far the most editions of any author were those of Aristotle's writings, often accompanied by the glosses of Averroës and other commentators.

The whole conception of nature was affected by the systematic atomism found in the full text of Lucretius' *De Rerum Natura* discovered in a monastery in 1417 by a humanist scholar, Poggio Bracciolini. Certainly Lucretius' ideas were not unknown before this date. They appear, for example, in the writing of Hrabanus Maurus, William of Conches, and Nicholas of Autrecourt. But Lucretius' poem seems to have been known only in part, in quotations in the books of grammarians. It was printed later in the 15th century and thereafter many times.

Not only mathematics and physical science, but also biology, benefited from the texts and translations published by the humanists. The humanist press made readily available the works of authors who had been either, like Celsus (*fl.* 14–37 A.D.), previously unknown or, like Theophrastus, known only through secondary sources, and new translations of Aristotle and Galen and of Hippocrates. The last came to replace Galen as the chief medical guide, greatly to the advantage of empirical practice. Pliny's *Natural History* was printed many times and Dioscorides' *De Materia Medica* twice, and there were many editions of Arabic medical writers in Latin translation: Avicenna, Rhazes, Mesue, Serapion. The new texts acted as a stimulus to the study of biology in what was at first a very curious way, for not the least important motive was the desire of humanist scholars, with their excessive adulation of antiquity, to identify animals, plants and minerals mentioned by classical authors. The limitations of this motive were eventually made evident by the very biological studies which it inspired, for these revealed the limitations of classical knowledge, and this was shown still further by the new fauna and flora discovered as a result of geographical exploration, by the increasing practical knowledge of anatomy being acquired by the surgeons, and by the brilliant advances in biological illustration stimulated by naturalistic art. But the original humanist motive draws attention to a feature of 16th- and early 17th-century science in nearly all its branches which historians of science of an earlier generation than the present would have been inclined to associate rather with the preceding centuries; for it was just this extravagant reverence for the ancients, just this devotion to the texts of Aristotle or Galen, that provoked the sarcastic hostility of the contemporary scientists who were trying to use their eyes to look at the world in a new way. And the beginning of this new science dates from the 13th century.

The principal original contributions made during the Middle Ages to the development of natural science in Europe may be summarised as follows:

1. In the field of scientific method, the recovery of the Greek idea of theoretical explanation in science, and especially of the "Euclidean" form of such explanation and its use in mathematical physics, raised the problems of how to construct and to verify or falsify theories. The basic conception of scientific explanation held by the medieval natural scientists came from the Greeks and was essentially the same as that of modern science. When a phenomenon had been accurately described so that its

characteristics were adequately known, it was explained by relating it to a set of general principles or theories connecting all similar phenomena. The problem of the relation between theory and experiment presented by this form of scientific explanation was analysed by the scholastics in developing their methods of "resolution and composition." Examples of the use of the scholastic methods of induction and experiment are seen in optics and magnetics in the thirteenth and fourteenth centuries. The methods involved everyday observations as well as specially devised experiments, simple idealisations, and "thought experiments," but also mention of imaginary and impossible experiments.

2. Another important contribution to scientific method was the extension of mathematics to the whole of physical science, at least in principle. Aristotle had restricted the use of mathematics, in his theory of the subordination of one science to another, by sharply distinguishing the explicative roles of mathematics and "physics." The effect of this change was not so much to destroy this distinction as to change the kind of question scientists asked. One principal reason for the change was the influence of the Neoplatonic conception of nature as ultimately mathematical, a conception exploited in the notion that the key to the physical world was to be found in the study of light. Certainly the medieval scientists did not press this conception to the limit, but they did begin to show less interest in the "physical" or metaphysical question of cause and to ask the kind of question that could be answered by a mathematical theory within reach of experimental verification. Examples of this method are seen in mechanics, optics and astronomy in the 13th and 14th centuries. It was through the mathematicisation of nature and of physics that the inconvenient classical concept of pairs of opposites was replaced by the modern concept of homogeneous linear measures.

3. Besides these ideas on method, though often closely connected with them, a radically new approach to the question of space and motion began at the end of the 13th century. Greek mathematicians had constructed a mathematics of rest, and important advances in statics had been made during the 13th century, progress assisted by Archimedean methods of manipulating ideal quantities such as the length of the weightless arm of a balance. The 14th century saw the first attempts to construct a mathematics of change and motion. Of the various elements contributing to this new dynamics and kinematics, the ideas that space might be infinite and void, and the universe without a centre, undermined Aristotle's cosmos with its qualitatively different directions and led to the idea of relative motion. Concerning motion, the chief new idea was that of *impetus,* and the most significant characteristic of this concept was that a measure was given of the quantity of *impetus* in which this was proportional to the quantity of matter in the body and the velocity imparted to it. Also important was the discussion of the persistence of *impetus* in the absence of resistance from the medium and of the action of gravity. *Impetus* was still a "physical" cause in the Aristotelian sense; in considering motion as a state requiring no continuous efficient causation, Ockham made another contribution perhaps related to the 17th-century idea of inertial motion. The theory of *impetus* was used to explain many different phenomena, for instance the motion of projectiles and falling bodies, bouncing balls, pendulums and the rotation of the heavens or of the earth. The possibility of the last was suggested by the concept of relative motion, and objections to it from the argument from detached bodies were met by the idea of "compound motion" advanced by Oresme. The kinematic study of accelerated motion began also in the 14th century, and the solution of one particular problem, that of a body moving with uniform acceleration, was to be applied later to falling bodies. Discussions of the nature

of a continuum and of maxima and minima began also in the 14th century.

4. In the field of technology, the Middle Ages saw some remarkable progress. Beginning with new methods of exploiting animal-, water- and wind-power, new machines were developed for a variety of purposes, often requiring considerable precision. Some technical inventions, for instance the mechanical clock and magnifying lenses, were to be used as scientific instruments. Measuring instruments such as the astrolabe and quadrant were greatly improved as a result of the demand for accurate measurement. In chemistry, the balance came into general use. Empirical advances were made and the experimental habit led to the development of special apparatus.

5. In the biological sciences, some technical advances were made. Important works were written on medicine and surgery, on the symptoms of diseases, and descriptions were given of the flora and fauna of different regions. A beginning was made with classification, and the possibility of having accurate illustrations was introduced by naturalistic art. Perhaps the most important medieval contribution to theoretical biology was the elaboration of the idea of a scale of animated nature. In geology observations were made and the true nature of fossils understood by some writers.

6. Concerning the question of the purpose and nature of science, two medieval contributions may be singled out. The first is the idea, first explicitly expressed in the 13th century, that the purpose of science was to gain power over nature useful to man. The second is the idea insisted on by the theologians, that neither God's action nor man's speculation could be constrained within any particular system of scientific or philosophical thought. Whatever may have been its effects in other branches of thought, the effect of this idea on natural science was to bring out the relativity of all scientific theories and the fact that they might be replaced by others more successful in fulfilling the requirements of the rational and experimental methods.

Thus the experimental and mathematical methods were a growth, developing within the medieval system of scientific thought, which was to destroy from within and eventually to burst out from Aristotelian cosmology and physics. Though resistance to the destruction of the old system became strong among certain of the late scholastics, and especially among those whose humanism had given them too great a devotion to the ancient texts and those by whom the old system had been too closely linked with theological doctrines, there can be little doubt that it was the development of these experimental and mathematical methods of the 13th and 14th centuries that at least initiated the historical movement of the Scientific Revolution culminating in the 17th century.

But when all is considered, the science of Galileo, Harvey and Newton was not the same as that of Grosseteste, Albertus Magnus and Buridan. Not only were their aims sometimes subtly and sometimes obviously different and the achievements of the later science infinitely the greater; they were not in fact connected by an unbroken continuity of historical development. Towards the end of the 14th century, the brilliant period of scholastic originality came to an end. For the next century and a half all that Paris and Oxford produced on astronomy, physics, medicine or logic were dreary epitomes of the earlier writings. One or two original thinkers like Nicholas of Cusa and Regiomontanus appeared in Germany in the 15th century. Italy fared better but rather with the new group of "artist-engineers" like Leonardo da Vinci than in the universities. Interest and intellectual originality were directed towards literature and the plastic arts rather than towards natural science.

Apart from anything else, the enormously greater achievements and confidence of the

17th-century scientists make it obvious that they were not *simply* carrying on the earlier methods though using them better. But if there is no need to insist on the historical fact of a Scientific Revolution in the 17th century, neither can there be any doubt about the existence of an original scientific movement in the 13th and 14th centuries. The problem concerns the relations between them. Whatever may have happened earlier, must the new science of the 17th century after all be considered a completely new beginning, as some historians of the past have claimed? Did the "new philosophy," the "Physico-mathematical Experimental Learning" of the early Royal Society, spring unheralded from the heads of Galileo and Harvey and Francis Bacon and Descartes? Granting the great and fundamental differences between medieval and 17th-century science, the equally striking underlying similarities, apart from other evidence, indicate that a more accurate view of 17th-century science is to regard it as the second phase of an intellectual movement in the West that began when the philosophers of the 13th century read and digested in Latin translation the great scientific authors of classical Greece and Islam.

It may be asked then what the scientists of the 16th and 17th centuries in fact knew of the medieval work, and how the similarities and differences of their aims may be characterised?

As to the first question, the products of the early printing presses show that the principal medieval scientific writings were certainly made readily available, and this in turn indicates that there was an academic demand for them. The available data indicates, as would be expected, that the early presses of the late 15th and early 16th centuries, for example at Venice and Padua and Basel and Paris, continued to reproduce by the new process of printing the same kinds of writings that had formerly been reproduced by hand. A large proportion of these printed works were scientific, and consisted of editions of the writings of the standard classical, Arabic (in Latin translation), and medieval authors. A considerable improvement over the old manuscript copies was the publication of critical *opera omnia* in collected editions.

Although there were some notable exceptions, most of the most important medieval scientific writings were made available in print. Without going into elaborate details, these included, among the more philosophical authors, the principal writings on scientific method and philosophy of science by Grosseteste, Albertus Magnus, Aquinas, Roger Bacon, Duns Scotus, Burley, Ockham, Cusa, and the Italian Averroïsts from Pietro d'Abano down to Nifo and Zabarella in the early 16th century. The dynamical and kinematical writings of Bradwardine, Heytesbury, Richard Swineshead, Buridan, Albert of Saxony, and Marliani were all printed more than once, and so were some of the mathematical writings of Oresme, although not the important *De Configurationibus Intensionum* and *Livre du Ciel*. Dumbleton's writings also remained in manuscript. On statics the *Liber Jordani de Ponderibus* was published in 1533, and the *De Ratione Ponderis* of the "school" of Jordanus Nemorarius was published by Tartaglia, in 1565. On optics the writings of Grosseteste, Roger Bacon, Witelo (together with Alhazen's treatise), Pecham, and Themon Judæi all found publishers. The most notable exception was the *De Iride* of Theodoric of Freiberg, but an account of his theory of the rainbow with the essential diagrams was published in Erfurt in 1514. Petrus Peregrinus' *Epistola de Magnete* was printed twice in the 16th century, in 1558 and 1562, and also failed to find a publisher, but was nevertheless known to and acknowledged by Gilbert. The most popular astronomical text was Sacrobosco's *Sphere*, but astronomical tables and related mathematical writings like those of Jean de Linières, Jean de Murs, Peurbach and Regiomontanus were also printed in representative quantity. Chaucer's *Treatise on the Astrolabe* was printed, but Richard of Wallingford's manuscripts were not. Another very important mathematician whose writings escaped publication was Leonardo Fibonacci.

The most important medieval biologist was Albertus Magnus; his *De Animalibus* was printed and so were his geological and chemical writings. Among other printed biological works were *The Art of Falconry* of the Emperor Frederick II and the writings of Thomas of Cantimpré, Peter of Crescenzi and Conrad von Megenburg. The herbals of Rufinus and Rinio remained unprinted, but other works in this field were printed, notably Matthæus Sylvaticus' *Pandectæ,* and new herbals in Latin and in the vernacular were also issued by the presses. The most popular work on natural history was Bartholomew the Englishman's *On the Properties of Things.* On anatomy, surgery and medicine the treatises, for example, of Mondino, Guy de Chauliac, Arnald of Villanova, Gentile da Foligno, and John of Gaddesden were printed many times, in some cases in several languages. Other excellent writings in this field, like those of Henri de Mondeville and Thomas of Sarepta, remained unpublished. On chemistry and alchemy the writings of Arnald of Villanova and those attributed to Raymond Lull were printed. So also were a number of practical treatises on various subjects, those of Brunschwig, Agricola and Biringuccio including much of earlier chemical practice.

The extent to which the scientists of the period showed an interest in these medieval treatises varied with different individuals. In the 16th century the strong classical leanings of men like Copernicus and Vesalius perhaps prevented them from paying much attention in print to medieval authors, but other leading scientists certainly did so. For example the Italian anatomists Achillini and Berengario da Carpi wrote commentaries on Mondino's anatomy. The theory of *impetus* and other aspects of medieval dynamics, kinematics and statics were studied and taught by mathematicians and philosophers such as Tartaglia, Cardano, Benedetti, Bonamico

and the young Galileo himself. In England Dr. John Dee collected manuscripts especially of the mathematical and physical writings of Grosseteste, Roger Bacon, Pecham, Bradwardine and Richard of Wallingford, while Robert Recorde recommended the writings of Grosseteste and other Oxford writers to students of astronomy. Dee and Recorde and Thomas and Leonard Digges were early supporters of the Copernican theory, and all saw their work as a revival of the great days of Oxford in the 13th and 14th centuries. Leonard Digges, in describing his father's pioneering work on telescopes, acknowledged Roger Bacon as an authority in optics. Leonardo da Vinci, Maurolyco, Marc Antonio de Dominis, Giambattista della Porta, Johann Marcus Marci and Christopher Scheiner all referred in their optical writings to Roger Bacon, Witelo and Pecham. Kepler wrote a commentary on Witelo, correcting his tables of angles of refraction; Snell's work on the law of refraction seems to have been stimulated by the edition of Witelo and Alhazen by Frederick Risner in 1572; and many other 17th-century optical writers, for example Descartes himself, Fermat, James Gregory, Emanuel Maignan and Grimaldi used the same source. As for Descrates, he seldom mentioned those to whom he was indebted, but his *Météores* follows the exact order of the subjects of Aristotle's *Meteorology* and is in more ways than one the last of the medieval commentaries on that much glossed work.

Enough has been said to show that leading scientists of the 16th and early 17th centuries both knew and used the writings of their medieval predecessors. The story is the same in biology as in physics, where Albertus Magnus was the principal medieval writer. In the conceptions of scientific method and explanation the medieval part of the ancestry is equally visible, especially for example in Galileo's use of the methods of "resolution and composition" to elucidate the relation between theory and experiment and to develop the "Euclidean" form of scientific explanations. So it is also in the Neoplatonic conception of nature as ultimately mathematical, first exploited in the Middle Ages in Grosseteste's "cosmology of light" and apparent in different ways in the thought of Galileo, Kepler and Descartes. But did the scientists, especially of the 17th century, simply accept and continue the aims and methods of the scholastics? It will appear in greater detail in the chapter that follows that clearly they did much more. One characteristic may be singled out as indicating an essential difference.

The central doctrines of medieval science developed almost entirely within the context of academic discussions based at some stage, near or far, on the books used in university teaching. The commentaries and *quæstiones* on the subjects treated in these books may have travelled far from the originals of Aristotle or Ptolemy or Euclid or Alhazen or Galen; they never escaped from them altogether. It is true that the applications of academic sciences, such as of astronomy in determining the calendar and making proposals for its reforms, or of arithmetic in the work of the exchequer and of commercial houses, or of anatomy and physiology and chemistry in surgery and medicine, were put into practice outside the universities. It is true also that in other fields outside the university system altogether, for example in technology of different kinds and in art and architecture with their increasing tendency to naturalism, developments took place that were to be of profound importance for science. Certainly the reasons for the development of science within the universities, and for the growth and spread of the university system itself, must be related to the reasons for the development of national political states based on an expanding commercial capitalism that could give employment to the men responsible for these technological and artistic activities outside. The latter, becoming the "artist-engineers" of the 15th and 16th centuries and the *virtuosi* and independent scientific gentlemen

of the 17th, were to take over the leadership of science, making it more an activity of the Accademia dei Lincei or the Royal Society or the Académie Royale des Sciences than of the universities. This was true even though in these scientific societies there was a predominance of university men, who were in fact to bring the new science back into the universities themselves.

But in the 13th and 14th centuries it was within the framework of the university faculty of arts, its curriculum expanded to include the new translations from Greek and Arabic and some technical treatises on applied mathematics, and of the higher faculties of medicine and of theology, that the central conceptions of science were cultivated. The men who cultivated them were clerics and academic teachers. The academic exercise was never far away in the background of the treatises they have left behind, those unliterary writings that form the great collections of manuscripts and early printed books that show us their ways of thought. Certainly many of them were original and ingenious thinkers. But the great scientific and cosmological problems with which they dealt were seldom seen by them as purely scientific. The greatest problem of all was the relation of the cosmology of Christian theology based on revelation to the cosmology of rational science dominated by Aristotle's philosophy. Although some of the best medieval scientific work was done on particular problems studied without any reference to theology or philosophy or even methodology, it was within a general framework of philosophy closely bearing on theology, and specifically within the system of university studies run by clerics, that the central development of medieval science took place.

The result of this was that science in the Middle Ages was nearly always at the same time philosophy of science. No doubt the same characteristics will appear in any age that is still determining the direction and objectives of its inquiries, as they did eminently in the 17th century, for example in the scientific thought and controversies of Galileo, Descartes and Newton. In contrast with both medieval and 17th-century scientists, those of the 20th century know in general how they are going to deal with problems, the kinds of questions they are going to put to nature and the methods they will employ to get their answers. It is only in the profoundest and most general problems, when a line of explanation seems to meet with an *impasse,* that philosophy need nowadays disturb the even course of the bulk of the scientific work actually being done.

But there is one basic difference between the aims of medieval philosophy of science and of all the philosophy of science since Galileo. The latter is *primarily* concerned with clarifying and facilitating the processes and further advances of science itself. The main interest of scientists since Galileo has been in the ever-increasing range of concrete problems that science can solve, and if philosophical investigations are undertaken by scientists, it is usually because certain concrete and specific scientific problems can be satisfactorily solved only by a thorough reform of fundamental principles. The essays in philosophy by Galileo and Newton had essentially this purpose. But medieval and natural philosophers were *primarily* interested less in the concrete problems of the world of experience than in the *kind of knowledge* natural science was, how it fitted into the general structure of their metaphysics, and, if it extended so far, how it bore on theology. Many scientific problems were discovered as analogies that could illuminate a theological problem, as was the case with instrumental causality and the theory of *impetus.* Being taken up in the interests of something else, this was no doubt one reason why in the course of development they were so often so peremptorily dropped.

The contrast is one of general emphasis and is certainly not exclusive. In the 18th century Berkeley and Kant, for example, were primarily concerned not with science but with the bearing of Newtonian cosmology on metaphysics, while in the 13th century Jordanus, Gerard of Brussels and Petrus Peregrinus seem to have been innocent of any philosophical interests and purely concerned with the immediate scientific problems in hand. But if what has been said does truly characterise the general intellectual ambience of medieval science, it explains much that is puzzling and seemingly downright perverse in otherwise excellent work. It helps to explain, for example, the gap between the repeated insistence on the principle of empirical verification and the many general assertions never tested by observation; worse, the satisfaction with imaginary experiments either incorrect or impossible; even worse, the false figures given, for example, by scientists of the calibre of Witelo or Theodoric of Freiberg allegedly as the results of measurements plainly never made. There are of course examples of medieval science not marred by such defects, but it was a peculiarity of the period that they could occur in the course of even the best-conceived investigations. The impression is left that the investigator was not strongly interested in mere details of fact and measurement. Certainly the strong interest in the theory and logic of experimental science and in related philosophical conceptions of nature, sustained from Grosseteste down to the threshold of Galileo's activities, stands in striking contrast with the comparative scarcity of actual experimental investigations. This becomes intelligible if we see the medieval natural philosophers not as modern scientists *manqués* but as primarily philosophers. They gave an account of experimental inquiries often as an exercise in what could be done in one branch of philosophy in distinction from others. Certainly this had the desirable effect of clarifying the problems of natural science and helping to extricate them from alien contexts of metaphysics and theology. In what was actually found out by experiment they were less interested.

It was a direction of interest that could have been fatal to Western science. Excellent as may have been much of their general characterisation of the methodology of experimental science, it meant that the methodologists seldom really put their methods to the practical test. So they rarely made them really precise or really adequate. Undirected experiments and simple everyday observations abound in the work of medieval scientists. Certainly there was no general movement to conceive of experimental inquiry as a sustained testing of a series of precisely and quantitatively formulated hypotheses, pressing on to the reformulation of a whole area of theory. The examples of experimental inquiries, even the best of them, remained isolated without general effect on the accepted doctrines of light or of cosmology. They were thought sufficient to illustrate the method, and methodology was an end in itself. It would have become a dead end had not Galileo and his contemporaries, with a new direction of interest, pursued the subjects of the examples for their own sakes. It was through taking these seriously, through paying attention to the detailed facts of experiment and measurement and mathematical functions actually exemplified in nature, that the 17th-century scientists were led to their radical revolution in the whole theoretical framework of physics and cosmology, where the medieval natural philosophers had only revised some limited sections.

If it is true that a fundamental change in the interests of scientists and in the conception of science can be charted about the time of Galileo, a further point would indicate another detail of the general line of change. Perhaps the most powerful feature of the medieval philosophy of science that remained strongly influential in the early 17th century was the Neoplatonic conception that nature was ultimately to be explained by mathematics. In the Middle Ages this belief was exploited mainly in the field of optics. Within the ambience of Platonism, and encouraged by the story in *Genesis* of the first day of creation, leading thinkers of the 13th and 14th centuries focussed their attention on the study of light as the key to the mysteries of the physical world, and in optics they did some of their best scientific work. But, as in the Aristotelian classification, optics remained, together with astronomy and music, one of the *mathematica media,* mathematical sciences applied to the physical world as distinct on the one hand from pure mathematics, and on the other from physics as the science of "natures" and causes. Medieval scientists seemed to feel no overwhelming desire or need to dispense with these philosophical distinctions. Mathematical physics never really became a universal science rendering Aristotelian physics unnecessary.

Perhaps it was pointed of Descartes, the most medieval of the great 17th-century scientists in the sense of being the most dominated by a philosophy of nature, to call his reforming work on cosmology *Le Monde, ou Traité de la Lumière.* But Descartes' physics were not based on a theory of light; rather his theory of light was based on his conception of motion. It was in the study of motion and not of light that the 17th-century scientists looked for the key to physics. It was there too that to their satisfaction they found it.

Certainly in giving special weight to the study of motion as distinct from other aspects of nature the 17th-century physicists made a fortunate choice. But Aristotle and the medieval Aristotelians had already made the study of motion the basis of their physics. The choice made by the 17th-century scientists was not fortuitous, nor was the success with which it was exploited. By taking the empirical phenomena of motion seriously as a problem and seeing the solution through to the end, they had no alternative but to reform the whole of cosmology, to invent new mathematical techniques in the process, and to provide the eminent example for the methods of science as a whole. This, it may be suggested, was the advance made by the secular *virtuosi* of the 17th century over the clerics of the medieval universities to whom in other ways they owed so much.

RENAISSANCE SCIENCE AS SEEN BY BURCKHARDT AND HIS SUCCESSORS

Ever since 1939, when he published his translation of *Three Copernican Treatises* (rev. ed., 1959), Edward Rosen (1906–   ) has been writing detailed monographic studies on Renaissance astronomy and optics. This long acquaintance with major currents in Renaissance scientific thought eminently qualifies him to serve as a spokesman for the Burckhardtian conception of Renaissance science.

Rosen received his doctorate from Columbia University. He is Professor of the History of Science at the City University of New York.

SINCE BURCKHARDT FELT so strong a revulsion against medieval life, and since he made no special study of the scientific work done during the Renaissance which he admired so much, it is not surprising that he altogether ignored the science of the Middle Ages. Although this or that isolated medieval scientist or scientific achievement had previously attracted the attention of other scholars, the first systematic investigation of the scientific writings composed during the Middle Ages was undertaken by a Frenchman who was born one year after Burckhardt published the first edition of his famous essay. Bringing to his task a burning zeal, an astounding indefatigability, and that rare combination, thorough mastery of modern science coupled with intimate knowledge of the classical languages, Pierre Duhem challenged Burckhardt's palimpsest theory of the Renaissance:

The mechanical and physical science of which modern times are justly proud unfolds, through an uninterrupted series of barely perceptible improvements, from the doctrines taught in the medieval schools. The proclaimed intellectual revolutions were most frequently merely slow evolutions, long in preparation; the so-called renaissances were only reactions, often unjust and sterile. Respect for tradition is an essential condition of scientific progress.

It was Duhem's contention, vigorously enunciated over and over again, that modern science was born in the medieval universities, from which it has developed in an unbroken line. Then if Duhem was right, in the field of science there was no Renaissance.

This anti-Burckhardtian thesis was asserted by Duhem at first with regard to the modern science of statics which, he claimed, "was derived . . . from the science that was born about the year 1200." He chose this date of birth because it was then that Jordanus Nemorarius demonstrated the law of the lever by using the postulate that equal force is necessary to raise different weights to heights inversely proportional to their weights. "The first germ" of this principle, said Duhem, is found in the treatise of Jordanus, who must therefore be regarded as the founder of the science of statics.

But when Duhem glanced back at antiquity, he remembered that the unknown

From Edward Rosen, "Renaissance Science as Seen by Burckhardt and His Successors," pp. 80–98. Reprinted with permission of the copyright owners, the Regents of the University of Wisconsin, from *The Renaissance: A Reconsideration of the Theories and Interpretations*, Tinsley Helton, ed., 1961, The University of Wisconsin Press.

author of the *Mechanical Problems* long attributed to Aristotle "would deserve to be celebrated as the father of rational mechanics," and that Archimedes "founded statics." A later student of this subject, Professor Marshall Clagett, was convinced "that the principle of virtual velocities, in a germinal form, at least," was "used to account for a fundamental law of statics" in the pseudo-Aristotelian *Mechanical Problems,* and was expressed even more clearly in another ancient Greek treatise, Hero's *Mechanics.* With complete confidence in Professor Clagett's painstaking work, should we not therefore acknowledge, as Duhem did, that "the western Middle Ages had received, either directly or through the Arabs as intermediaries, the tradition of certain Greek theories about the lever and the Roman balance"? Then the founder of the science of statics turns out to have been, not Jordanus, but a nameless ancient Greek.

What was Jordanus' contribution to the science of statics? In a city of commercial importance at a time when extensive trade had recommenced, he revived a science useful in determining the right price of weighed merchandise. He cast his treatise in the ancient Greek geometrical form of postulates and theorems. His "seven postulates and nine theorems . . . were not originated by Jordanus but were inherited by him as a set of propositions supposedly derived from Euclid," according to the conjecture of his modern editor, Professor Ernest Addison Moody, who held that Jordanus supplied "the proofs of these inherited theorems." On the other hand, Miss Annaliese Maier believed that Jordanus supplied no proofs; these were rather the work of later thirteenth-century commentators writing about propositions propounded by Jordanus.

In either case, how does the history of the science of statics look? Must we not say: Greek origin, Islamic detour, Western Renaissance? Then, in statics, there was a Renaissance. It did not begin in Italy, nor in the fifteenth century. It did begin in a neighboring Mediterranean country in the thirteenth century.

Duhem's thesis that there were no renaissances turns out, on his own showing, to be wrong. What is more, he too believed in at least one fifteenth-century Italian renaissance: "Leonardo da Vinci . . . extending our knowledge of statics and dynamics beyond the point to which they had been carried by Aristotle and Archimedes, brought about the renaissance of mechanics." Leonardo was able to do so because "the mechanics of the peripatetics," according to Duhem, "slept for a long time in the bed in which it was wrapped up by the scholastic commentators." And Duhem recognized that Leonardo was only "one of those universal intellects produced by Italy with marvelous fecundity in the fifteenth and sixteenth centuries."

As we have just seen, Duhem denied that there were any renaissances in the same book in which he attributed to Leonardo da Vinci the renaissance of mechanics. With similar indifference to self-consistency, he asserted:

Science knows no spontaneous generation. The most unexpected discoveries were never created in their entirety by the mind which gave birth to them. They always came forth from a first germ which had been deposited in this genius. His function is limited to nourishing and developing the little seed planted in him until a tree with mighty foliage puts forth flowers and fruit.

In violation of his own principle that no scientific innovation is completely spontaneous, Duhem could say: "In the mechanical writings bequeathed to us by antiquity we find no trace of Jordanus' axiom; it seems to be a spontaneous product of western science."

The work of Jordanus and his followers was unjustly treated by sixteenth-century physicists, Duhem complained:

The innovators, or those who pretend to be innovators, are then so extreme that they wish to retain none of the achievements of the preceding ages. Everything connected closely or even distantly with peripatetic scholasticism seems to them basically false and pernicious. They reject it without examination, in order to preserve only the legacy left by the geometers of classical antiquity. These innovators, who weaken science by throwing out everything accomplished by the Middle Ages, we have seen at work when we studied the reaction led by Guido Ubaldo del Monte and by Giovanni Battista Benedetti against the school of Jordanus.

But Del Monte and Benedetti, so far from rejecting Jordanus "without examination," subjected him to an examination which Duhem himself reviewed for many pages.

In the course of his researches on the history of statics, Duhem became fascinated by that enigmatic genius, Leonardo da Vinci. While attempting to learn more about those authors whom Leonardo had read and about those who gained access to Leonardo's unpublished manuscripts, Duhem widened his anti-Renaissance view of the history of science to include that most important chapter of physics which goes by the name of mechanics.

In the preface to his third volume on Leonardo, which was originally published in 1913 and has since been reissued in 1955, Duhem wrote as follows:

The science of mechanics, inaugurated by Galileo, by his rivals, by his disciples . . . is not a creation. The modern mind did not produce it at once and altogether as soon as the reading of Archimedes had revealed to it the art of applying geometry to natural effects. The mathematical skill acquired by acquaintance with the geometers of antiquity was used by Galileo and his contemporaries to develop and make exact a science of mechanics whose principles had been laid down and most essential propositions formulated by the Christian Middle Ages. This mechanics was taught by the physicists at the University of Paris in the fourteenth century. . . . Galileo and his emulators were the heirs of this Parisian tradition. When we see the science of a Galileo triumph over peripateticism . . . in our ignorance of the history of human thought, we believe that we are witnessing the victory of youthful modern science over medieval philosophy, obstinate and parrot-like. Actually we are watching the

science which was born at Paris in the fourteenth century win out, after long preparation, over the doctrines of Aristotle and Averroes, which had been restored to honor by the Italian Renaissance.

In this connection the motion of a projectile is the key phenomenon. Consider the case of an arrow shot from a bow. Why does the arrow continue to fly through the air after it has left the bowstring? As an inanimate object, it cannot move itself, said Aristotle's interpreters: the arrow is pushed by the air, for there can be no vacuum in nature, and the air which is torn apart by the flying arrow re-unites immediately behind it; the force that causes a motion must be constantly in contact with the moving object; there can be no action at a distance.

In the fourteenth century a rival theory was put forward, most effectively by Jean Buridan, the famous Paris professor whose name is indissolubly but perhaps erroneously linked with the case of the undecided ass. In opposition to Aristotle, Buridan held that the air resists, not causes, the motion of the arrow; the bowstring imparts to the arrow at the instant of its release an incorporeal force, called "impetus," that keeps the arrow in motion after it has left the string; now the cause of the continued motion is no longer the outside medium, but is inside the moving object.

Obviously Buridan's impetus theory is far superior to Aristotle's imaginary "air engine." The impetus theory was characterized by Miss Maier as "an independent and special intermediate stage between Aristotelianism and modern natural science, a stage which stands closer to the former than to the latter." She emphasized the difference between the medieval notion of impetus and the modern concept of inertia. Impetus was considered an intrinsic tendency acting as a motive force within a moving body and causing the continuation of a motion that had previously been initiated by some external agent. By contrast, in his *Principes de la philosophie* Descartes said: "Once a body has begun to move, we must conclude that thereafter it continues to move and never stops by itself"; the modern concept of inertia requires no inherent force for the continuation of a motion, once it has begun. In the impetus theory, once a body has begun to move, it tends to stop; hence motion is a process requiring a cause not only to start it but also to continue it. But in Newton's first law, motion becomes a state or status, like rest: "Every body continues in its state of rest or of uniform motion in a straight line, unless it is compelled to change that state by forces impressed upon it." Just as nobody ever asks why a body at rest continues at rest, so in the inertial theory a body in motion continues to move. The continuation of inertial motion requires no such expenditure of energy as was ascribed to the impetus. In the inertial theory the application of a constant force, such as the earth's gravitational pull, produces a uniform acceleration; "on the other hand, it is one of the most important principles of scholastic mechanics that from a constant force a constant velocity follows." In the inertial theory, force is proportional to acceleration; in the impetus theory, force is proportional to velocity.

Thus we see that the impetus theory, although a step in the right direction, did not reach the correct conclusion. The precise historical relation between the impetus theory and modern physics will be determined when it is learned to what extent Galileo, Descartes, and their contemporaries were familiar with fourteenth-century mechanics. But at least this much is known about the earlier history of the impetus doctrine. It was not invented in the fourteenth century. It was first propounded by a Greek in opposition to Aristotle's theory of projectiles. The Greek idea of impetus was adopted by a number of influential Islamic thinkers. Did it re-enter Western civilization either directly or through the medium of a Muslim writer? If so, we recognize once more the pattern which we discerned previously in the history of statics: Greek origin and Western renaissance, with or without Islamic detour.

When the velocity of a moving body varies uniformly over a given distance, then its speed at the midpoint, if multiplied by the elapsed time, gives the distance traversed. This valuable rule was discovered at Merton College, Oxford, about 1330. Duhem maintained that in 1368 Albert of Saxony described the speed of a freely falling body as uniformly accelerated and that nearly two hundred years later Domingo de Soto applied the Merton theorem of uniform acceleration to the case of a freely falling body. De Soto's application was "casually suggested," says Clagett, who also calls it a deduction, for no reason evident to me. De Soto's casual suggestion, I may add, requires textual emendation; so does Albert's assertion of a freely falling body's uniform acceleration, which he both asserted and denied. Nevertheless, Duhem reasoned, "the physicists of the Paris school established all the foundations of mechanics which were developed later by Galileo, his contemporaries, and his disciples." Duhem's conclusion was that the Parisian doctors deserved to be saluted as the "precursors of Galileo."

For this undeniably correct conclusion Duhem invoked the testimony of Galileo himself, in whose youthful writings the "Parisian doctors" are twice cited by name. These two citations convinced Duhem that Galileo had studied the Paris doctors. But Duhem overlooked the warning issued by the editor of the national edition of Galileo's works that these youthful writings were the product of Galileo's hand, not of his brain; he was not their author, but only an amanuensis. The extensive erudition displayed in them is all by itself a decisive argument against his youthful authorship. The two citations prove that Galileo had heard of the Paris doctors, not that he had studied them. They were unquestionably precursors of Galileo, since they discussed mechanics before he did. But any influence of their discussions on him has to be found in the products of his own mind. Some of the documents needed for such an investigation have been made conveniently accessible by Clagett in his recent book *The Science of Mechanics in the Middle Ages,* where unfortunately he twice repeated Duhem's error in taking Galileo to be the author of works which he merely copied when he was a twenty-year-old student at the University of Pisa. Their true author was probably Francesco Buonamici, Galileo's teacher in philosophy, to whose opinions Galileo afterwards offered the most vigorous objections.

"The first valid solution of the problem of the force required to hold a weight in equilibrium on an inclined plane" was achieved in the thirteenth century, according to Moody. Did Galileo know about this thirteenth-century solution, or did he not? "He may well have discovered this solution without help or suggestion from his medieval predecessor," whose "theorems and proofs involve numerous errors and frequent obscurities," says Moody. A similar explanation accounts, in my opinion, for Galileo's neglect of Kepler's discovery that the orbit of a planet is elliptical. Galileo did not possess Duhem's enormous erudition. He was not an assiduous reader, preferring to consult what he liked to call the book of Nature. He reacted enthusiastically to the experimental and naturalistic investigations of William Gilbert. But he felt little sympathy for the long-winded theological speculations, mythological allusions, and autobiographical meanderings in which Kepler concealed his genuine achievement. Can we therefore accept Moody's assurance that "the historical continuity of the development of modern mechanics, from the small beginnings found in Jordanus de Nemore through the fourteenth-century 'impetus physics' and down to Galileo and his contemporaries, is discernible at each stage"? Can Moody, or any other follower of Duhem, really document "each stage" in this allegedly continuous development? Until such proof is forthcoming, shall we not rather heed Koyré, who maintains that Galileo's mathematical-experimental physics was an intellectual mutation, noncontinu-

ous with medieval physics, and Maier, who holds that the principle of inertia evolved, not out of, but in opposition to, the impetus theory?

A younger contemporary of Jean Buridan at the University of Paris, Nicole Oresme, singled out by Maier as "undoubtedly the greatest genius among the fourteenth-century philosophers of nature," was declared by Duhem to have been "the inventor of analytic geometry." To his question "Is it not proper to say that analytic geometry in two dimensions was created by Oresme?" the historian of mathematics, Heinrich Wieleitner, promptly and flatly answered "No." The basis of Duhem's claim was the supposed discovery by Oresme of the equation of the straight line. But that equation, even if its verbal equivalent in a generalized form be attributed to Oresme, did not appear until long after analytic geometry had established itself as one of the most important accomplishments of the seventeenth century. Moreover, can Duhem's claim that Oresme invented analytic geometry be reconciled with his admission that Oresme possessed only a "very rudimentary knowledge of mathematics"? The *Treatise on Proportions* by Thomas Bradwardine, another fourteenth-century mathematician, "bristles with inconsistencies and internal contradictions," says Professor Eduard Jan Dijksterhuis, who adds that "the level of ancient Greek mathematics was infinitely higher than that of Bradwardine's time, and the latter owes all the value it possesses to the former."

Despite the low level of Oresme's mathematical attainments, he did make a lasting contribution, without really intending to do so, to what may be termed the expository side of mathematics. As a step in a direction looking far beyond mathematics, Oresme showed how the changes in a variable could be graphically depicted by connecting points placed at the proper distances from two intersecting straight lines. But his deficiency in geometrical knowledge and algebraic technique prevented him from taking full advantage of his facility in handling linear and broken-line graphs. Oresme's straight lines extended only in the positive direction; he had no functional conception of coördinates, and certainly not of negative coördinates, which were introduced by Isaac Newton. Oresme's variables were not actually measured; many of them still cannot be measured. The aspect of his graphs which interested Oresme was the shape of the plane figure under the line connecting the plotted points, not the line itself. He failed to understand that the upper boundary line of his geometrical figure could be expressed by an algebraic equation in two variables, and that conversely any such equation determined a specific line or curve. In other words, he did not systematically associate algebra with geometry; that association is of course the distinguishing characteristic of analytic geometry. Oresme's geometry was Euclidean, not analytic.

In determining the shape of the geometrical figure appropriate to a given rate of change, Oresme believed that he was discovering, not a useful mathematical tool, but a fact of nature. Thus, for him a uniform acceleration is not merely *represented* by a triangle or trapezoid; it *is* in physical reality a triangle or trapezoid. These geometrical figures were thought by Oresme to be no mere mathematical abstractions, but to produce effects in the real world: if a plant or stone had the shape of a heart, it would cure heart disease; the friendship of man and dog could be explained by the compatibility of their geometrical figures, etc. Each geometrical figure was unique and invariant, forming part of the object's or quality's essence. It could not be modified by the mathematician's arbitrary choice of scale or parameter.

Obviously all this has nothing whatever in common with analytic geometry. That indispensable branch of modern mathematics was invented, not by Oresme (despite Duhem), but by another ingenious Frenchman almost three hundred years his junior. How did René Descartes come to invent analytic geometry? His attention was called to a problem solved only partially by the late Greek geometer, Pappus of Alexandria, an author unknown to the medieval Latin West. And if Pierre Fermat, who in his self-proclaimed indolence refrained from publishing his discovery, is nevertheless to be regarded as a coinventor of analytic geometry, he, too, was a close student of the ancient Greek mathematicians and their Renaissance continuators such as François Viète. In short, analytic geometry omits the second stage of our previous triads: here we pass without any Islamic detour directly from ancient Greece to modern Western Europe, leaping over the uneventful intervening centuries.

In Duhem's scale of values both mathematics and physics, despite their great importance, ranked below astronomy. Hence for him the history of science turned a sharp corner when the impetus theory was extended from terrestrial physics to celestial dynamics:

If we wished to separate the realm of ancient science from the domain of modern science by a precise line, we should have to draw that line, I believe, at the instant when . . . the heavenly bodies ceased to be regarded as moved by divine beings, when the celestial motions and the sublunar motions were recognized to be dependent on the same mechanics.

Duhem's crucial instant, when the impetus theory was extrapolated from the earth to the heavens, occurred in the fourteenth century, presumably in its second quarter. The extrapolator, our old friend Buridan, assumed that God created the universe, and while doing so gave the heavenly bodies a push which has kept them moving at a constant rate ever since, because they encounter no resistance. Buridan's theory dispensed with the pagan intelligences or Christian angels which had been engaged, according to previous theories such as Aquinas' and Dante's, in constantly shoving the heavenly bodies around without ever becoming tired. Instead of all this unceasing effort, Buridan invoked a first divine push to get all the heavenly bodies started rolling. Hence all celestial motion was still attributed by Buridan to a supernatural, not a natural, cause. But in his view terrestrial motions arise from natural causes, such as the release of bent or twisted inanimate objects, and ultimately the muscular energy of animate beings. Hence, despite Duhem, celestial motions and sublunar motions were, for Buridan, only in part dependent on the same mechanics; in part they were dependent on different mechanics. The reunification of the universe, which had been sundered in twain by the mistaken Aristotelian cosmology, had to await a greater than Buridan.

Not long after Buridan extended the impetus theory to astronomy, his younger Paris contemporary Oresme, at whose contributions to mathematics we have already glanced, discussed the possibility of the earth's rotation. Duhem declared that Oresme was "a precursor of Copernicus; he actually maintained that to suppose the heavens motionless and the earth endowed with a daily motion of rotation was much more probable than to follow the contrary hypothesis." Let us test the reliability of Duhem's statement about Oresme. In 1377 Oresme translated into French, and wrote a commentary on, Aristotle's principal work on astronomy. In Book II of Oresme's *Le Livre du ciel et du monde,* Chapter 25 was entirely devoted to the question whether the earth does or does not move. After a most elaborate discussion, Oresme concluded:

Everybody maintains and I believe that the heavens move in this manner and the earth does not move (God established the earth, which will not be moved), notwithstanding the reasons to the contrary, for they are arguments which evidently are not conclusive. But considering everything that has been said, one could on that ground believe that the earth moves in this way and not the heavens, the contrary not being evident. And yet this seems on its face as much or even more against natural reason than are the articles of our faith, either all or some of them. And thus what I have said for fun in this manner can serve to refute and repel those who would wish to impugn our faith with reasons.

Oresme's *Le Livre du ciel* was not printed until 1943, when its editors pointed out that Duhem's "exaggerated claims" were based "entirely upon this gloss [which] contains really nothing to support Duhem's thesis." Duhem's characterization of Oresme's discussion as a "dissertation in favor of the earth's daily motion" is the very opposite of the truth, as is likewise Moody's statement that Oresme adopted the theory of the diurnal rotation of the earth. Like Aristotle and Ptolemy, Oresme considered and rejected the possibility of the earth's motion. Unlike the Greeks, however, who treated the topic seriously, Oresme did it for fun. The argument to which he attached the greatest importance was the quotation from Psalms 93:1. His principal purpose was to defend against rational attack his religious faith, which he recognized was entirely or mainly irrational. Thus he was essentially a theologian rather than a scientist.

Now let us compare Copernicus with Oresme. About a century and a half intervened between Oresme's *Le Livre du ciel* and Copernicus' *De revolutionibus orbium cœlestium.* Like Oresme, Copernicus was a churchman, yet no Biblical text decided any scientific question for him. He recalled that the church father Lactantius had ridiculed those who believed the earth was round. Copernicus made an eloquent plea for freedom of thought. Asserting the physical reality of the earth's motion, he asked to be protected from reprisals by theologians and commentators on Aristotle.

Had Copernicus read Oresme? There is no convincing evidence for an affirmative answer to this question. Like his precursors Copernicus listed ancient thinkers, and he utilized the observational results obtained by outstanding Muslim astronomers. Does not the relation between Oresme and Copernicus once more exemplify the conclusion we reached before: Greek origin, Islamic detour, Western renaissance?

Buridan rejected the earth's motion on the ground that it was "in conflict with the authority of Aristotle," and he dispensed with intelligences as the movers of the celestial bodies on the ground that these intelligences were not mentioned in the Bible. But modern science, like ancient Greek thought, recognizes no sacred book and no final authority. The scientist does not profess to have attained the absolute truth. His basic attitude is skeptical, not dogmatic. He welcomes the challenge of a new hypothesis. The history of science has taught him that errors are eliminated by subjecting rival theories to the test of evidence. His self-correcting discipline advances by appealing to those whose intellectual development qualifies them to sit in judgment. Precisely because no final dogma is at stake, no dissenter is burned to death or thrown into prison, nor are his books destroyed by fire, nor is he coerced into abjuring, whether sincerely or insincerely, his innermost convictions. Such desperate measures are not needed to defend tentative approximations to the truth or truths demonstrated beyond cavil.

Duhem thought otherwise. With Thomas Aquinas, he held that "in order to show that an astronomical hypothesis is in conformity with the nature of things, it is necessary not only to prove that it is sufficient to explain the phenomena, but also to demonstrate that the phenomena could not be explained if the hypothesis were abandoned or modified." Since Copernicus and Galileo could not possibly have eliminated every conceivable rival hypothesis, Duhem condemned them for asserting that Copernicanism was true. He wrote that "logic was on the side of Osiander and Bellarmine [who] grasped the exact significance of the experimental method"; that "despite Kepler and Galileo, we believe today, with Osiander and Bellarmine, that the hypotheses of physics are only mathematical devices designed to explain the phenomena." How did Duhem's fellow-fictionalists contribute to the advancement of science? Osiander was the Lutheran preacher who inserted the false preface in Copernicus' masterpiece, and Cardinal Bellarmine was the Jesuit theologian who ordered Galileo to abandon Copernicanism.

Not content to start modern science in the fourteenth century, in the seventh volume of his *Système du monde,* which was first published in 1956, forty years after his death, Duhem pushed the replacement of ancient Aristotelianism by modern science back into the thirteenth century:

Those who in the sixteenth century were aware of this substitution of one science for another were seized by a strange delusion. They imagined that this substitution had been sudden and that it was their work. They proclaimed that peripatetic physics, the dark haunt of error, had just crumbled under their blows and that on the ruins of this physics they had constructed, as though by magic, the clear abode of truth. Of the sincere delusion or haughtily intentional error of these persons, the men of the following centuries were the dupes or accomplices. The physicists of the sixteenth century were hailed as creators to whom the world owed the renaissance of the sciences; very often they were only continuators and sometimes plagiarists.

The destruction of Aristotelianism resulted, not from experiential testing of its propositions, but from philosophical discussions. These, according to Duhem, were

generally the product of a desire to accept nothing as true which is not in conformity with Catholic orthodoxy, of an anxiety not to incur condemnation proclaimed by ecclesiastical authority. One may say that the excommunications announced at Paris on March 7, 1277 by Bishop Étienne Tempier and by the doctors in theology were the birth certificate of modern physics.

Yet Duhem acknowledged that what followed the excommunications of 1277 was "not a new physics, more accurately based on experience, but theology. Isn't this fact perfectly clear to anybody who notices that most of the objections to Aristotle's dynamics were raised by professors of theology when their commentary on the *Sentences* led them to discuss the movement of the angels?" In Aristotle's dynamics motion was accomplished against the resistance of a medium, but the medium through which the angels moved offered no resistance to the movement of these figments of the religious imagination.

Peter Lombard's *Sentences* said that "in man, love increases and diminishes, and at different times it is more and less intense." It was the discussion of this famous theological text that ultimately led to Oresme's rectangular coördinates for exhibiting the intensification and attenuation of qualities. But these qualities can only be intuited by human thought; like angels, they cannot be weighed and measured.

Buridan, Duhem's alternate founder of modern science, who, like all other arts professors at the University of Paris, had to take an oath to decide all questions touching faith in accordance with faith, wrote that

a sailor who goes down to the bottom of the sea does not feel the weight of the water, even though he has on his shoulders a hundred or a thousand tons; for the water which is above him has no tendency to go any farther down.

A disciple of Oresme reports

this result of experience. Certain persons say that the magnet, together with the iron which it attracts, weighs no more than if it were alone.

He then proceeds, Duhem points out, to

deduce consequences from this statement without thinking that there would be reason to test its accuracy and that it would be quite easy for him to prove its falsity. In that respect Henry of Langenstein resembles those around him. All his contemporaries accept the least authenticated hearsay with the same credulity; they never submit it to the test of observation.

Is this the reason why medieval mechanics declined almost immediately after it started? Who extended the use of alphabetic letters after Jordanus Nemorarius introduced them to replace numbers in arithmetical calculations? Who developed Oresme's graphs? Why did the magnificent work of Frederick II on ornithology, or of Peter the Stranger on the magnet, or of Theodore of Freiberg on the rainbow, find no worthy successor? Why did Oresme, in discussing the possibility of the earth's motion, confine himself to the daily rotation and never think of attributing the annual revolution to the earth? Of this idea, said Duhem, "none of our Paris physicists seems to have had the least inkling. We should not be astonished by this; Archimedes' *Sand-Reckoner* was then unknown." Could there be any better confirmation of Burckhardt's thesis than this candid admission by his most outspoken opponent in the history of science?

Toward the end of his life Duhem was able to view medieval science more objectively, as can be seen in the following excerpt from the tenth and last volume of his *Système du monde*, which was published in 1959:

In order to make explicit all the wealth of ideas contained implicitly in the doctrines of Oresme, Buridan, and their contemporaries, first it was necessary to gain a more complete and more profound knowledge of mathematics than that with which these masters had had to be content. Then experimental instruments and methods which permit bodies and their motions to be studied with greater precision had to be available. In almost every domain the fourteenth-century Parisians had pushed ahead as far as anyone could go who possessed only the elements of arithmetic and geometry and who, for the purposes of observation, had only his five naked senses. Just as badly equipped, their fifteenth-century heirs could go no further than they did. For the doctrines whose seeds had been planted by Oresme and Buridan to flower and bear fruit, first it was necessary that to the knowledge of Euclid's *Elements* should be added a mastery of the more advanced methods created by Archimedes; to revive them and recover their use was the task of the sixteenth century. Then the physicists had to acquire the art of making precise and delicate measurements with the aid of instruments. This art was revealed to them by Galileo's century. So long as these two progressive steps had not been taken, scholastic physics could not pass beyond the boundary to which the fourteenth-century Parisians had brought it.

When Duhem, the arch-opponent of Burckhardt, reached a vantage point from which he could look back over his beloved fourteenth century and forward to the sixteenth and seventeenth centuries, to all intents and purposes he withdrew his objections to Burckhardt's thesis of a renaissance in science and gave it his valuable, though grudging, support.

A low mathematical level and lack of observational instruments were not the only ailments afflicting medieval science. Its mental outlook suffered from being directed more toward victory in debate than toward the search for the truth. After William Heytesbury, chancellor of Oxford University in 1371, lent his great prestige to the fashion, says Duhem,

the desire to discover in any and every place opportunities to prove oneself a skillful dialectician by resolving complicated sophisms did not take long to invade all studies. The scholastic method was only too favorable to this attitude of mind. . . .

Since Duhem's death Miss Annaliese Maier has emerged as the foremost student of medieval science. Although she has corrected many of Duhem's mistakes and has differed with him on a number of basic issues, she is in fundamental agreement with his final estimate of the Schoolmen. . . .

It is time to return to our opening question, How has the past century evaluated Renaissance science? Burckhardt with his limited knowledge stands at the start of the century. Vastly more learned investigators mark its close. Yet does not their answer to our question in substance repeat Burckhardt's answer?

THE SOCIAL AND ECONOMIC ROOTS
OF NEWTON'S "PRINCIPIA"

BORIS M. HESSEN

Boris Mikhailovich Hessen (or Gessen) (1883–1937?), an influential Soviet Marxist philosopher of the 1920's, is best known in the West for his socio-economic interpretation of Newton's *Principia*. However, his major work in the U.S.S.R. was concerned with the philosophy, rather than the history, of science, and the central figure in that work was Einstein, not Newton. As a specialist in the philosophy of physics he became involved in the factional debates of the late 1920's over the place of Einsteinian physics in the emerging Soviet Marxist philosophy of the natural sciences. Hessen aligned himself with the followers of Abram M. Deborin and led the Deborinites to accept the theory of relativity as the realization of dialectical materialism in physics. Although he experienced some rebuffs, Hessen maintained his position as a leading Soviet interpreter of modern physics through the early 1930's and was rewarded with the directorship of the Physical Institute of Moscow University. During the Stalinist purges of 1937, Hessen was unable to survive the new shifts in ideology. He was denounced as an enemy of the people and subsequently disappeared from the scene.

The Social and Economic Roots of Newton's "Principia" is not a typical work of Boris Hessen, nor is it a representative example of Soviet scholarship in the history of science. It is an occasional piece written to awaken Western scholars to the significance of the economic and social origins of science and to demonstrate to Soviet authorities that the author concurred with the government's current viewpoint toward scientists. Both of these aims were accomplished by Hessen's adoption of an extreme version of economic determinism. Despite its origins, Hessen's essay on Newton was to exert a strong influence upon the study of the history of science in the West. Some scholars immediately embraced this interpretation, others rejected it outright, while still others were able to extract from it the significant lesson that scientific activity is related to the social and economic structure of a nation. The exact nature of the relationship between science and the socio-economic structure has not yet been revealed.

Marx's Theory of the Historical Process

THE WORK and also the personality of Newton have attracted the attention of scientists of all ages and nations. The enormous extent of his scientific discoveries, the significance of his work to all the later developments of physics and technology, the notable exactitude of his laws justifiably arouse special respect for his genius.

What placed Newton at the turning-point of the development of science and gave him the possibility of indicating the new roads of this progressive movement?

Where are we to seek the source of Newton's creative genius? What determined the content and the direction of his activities?

These are the questions which inevitably confront the investigator who takes as his

From Boris M. Hessen, "The Social and Economic Roots of Newton's 'Principia,'" *Science at the Cross Roads* (London, n.d.), pp. 151–176.

task not the simple assembly of materials relating to Newton, but who wishes to penetrate into the very essence of his creative work.

Nature and nature's laws lay hid in night; God said "Let Newton be!" and all was light.

Said Pope, in a well-known couplet. . . . Thus the phenomenon of Newton is regarded as due to the kindness of divine providence, and the mighty impulse which his work gave to the development of science and technology is regarded as the result of his personal genius.

In this lecture we present a radically different conception of Newton and his work.

Our task will consist in applying the method of dialectical materialism and the conception of this historical process which Marx created, to an analysis of the genesis and development of Newton's work in connection with the period in which he lived and worked.

We give a brief exposition of the basic assumptions put forward by Marx which will be the guiding assumptions of our lecture. . . . We shall attempt to give the essence of the Marxian viewpoint as far as possible in his own words.

Society exists and develops as an organic whole. In order to ensure that existence and development society must develop production. In social production people enter into definite inter-relationships which are independent of their own will. At every given stage these relationships correspond to the development of the material productive forces. . . .

The method of production of material existence conditions the social, political and intellectual process of the life of society. . . .

In class society the ruling class subjects the productive forces to itself and, by virtue of its domination of material force, subjects all other classes to its interests.

The ideas of the ruling class in every historical period are the ruling ideas, and the ruling class distinguishes its ideas from all previous ideas by putting them forward as eternal truths. It wishes to reign eternally and bases the inviolability of its rule on the eternal quality of its ideas.

In capitalist society a separation of the dominating ideas from the production relationships occurs, and thus is created the view that the material structure is determined by ideas.

Practice has not to be explained by reference to ideas, but on the contrary the formation of ideas has to be explained by reference to material practice. . . .

The Marxist's analysis of Newton's activity, made on the basis of the foregoing assumptions, will consist first and foremost in understanding Newton, his work and his world outlook as the product of this period.

The Economics, Physics and Technology of Newton's Period

The general symptom of that section of world history which has come to be known as mediæval and modern history is first and foremost that during this period we have the rule of private property.

All the social and economic formations of this period preserve this basic symptom.

Consequently Marx regarded this period of the history of humanity as the history of the development of forms of private property, and distinguishes three subsidiary periods within the larger epoch.

The first period is that of the rule of feudalism. The second period begins with the disintegration of the feudal system and is characterised by the emergence and development of merchant capital and manufacture.

The third period in the history of the development of private property is that of the rule of industrial capitalism. It gives birth to large-scale industry, the application of the forces of nature to industrial purposes, mechanisation and the most detailed division of labour.

The brilliant successes of natural science during the sixteenth and seventeenth centuries were conditioned by the disintegration of the feudal economy, the development of merchant capital, of international maritime relationships and of heavy (mining) industry. . . .

Newton's activities fall within the second period in the history of the development of private property.

Consequently we investigate first and foremost the historical demands imposed by the emergence of merchant capital and of its development.

Then we consider what technical problems the newly developing economy raised for solution and we investigate to what grouping of physical problems and of science necessary to the solution of those problems these technical problems led.

We direct our survey to three outstanding spheres which were of decisive importance to the social and economic system we are investigating. These spheres are ways and means of communication, industry, and military affairs.

WAYS OF COMMUNICATION

. . . The development of merchant capital broke down the isolation of the town and the village commune, extended the geographical horizon to an extraordinary extent, and considerably accelerated the tempo of existence. It had need of convenient ways of communication, more perfect means of communication, a more exact measurement of time, especially in connection with the continually accelerating rate of exchange, and exact application of accounting and measuring.

Particular attention was directed to water transport: to maritime transport as a means of linking up various countries and to river transport as an internal link.

The development of river transport was also assisted by the fact that in antiquity waterways were the most convenient and most investigated, and the natural growth of the towns was linked up with the system of river communications. Transport over the rivers was three times as cheap as haulage transport.

The construction of canals also developed as a complementary means of internal transport and in order to link up the maritime transport with the internal river system.

Thus the development of merchant capital set transport the following technical problems:

IN THE REALM OF WATER TRANSPORT

1. An increase in the tonnage capacity of vessels and in their speed.
2. An improvement in the vessels' floating qualities: their reliability, sea-worthiness, their lesser tendency to rock, response to direction and ease of manœuvring, which was especially important for war-vessels.
3. Convenient and reliable means of determining position at sea. Means of determining the latitude and longitude, magnetic deviation, times of tides.
4. The perfecting of the internal waterways and their linking up with the sea; the construction of canals and locks.

INDUSTRY

Already by the end of the middle ages (14th and 15th centuries) the mining industry was developing into a large industry. The mining of gold and silver in connection with the development of currency circulation was stimulated by the growth of exchange. . . .

The powerful development of the war industry, which had made enormous advances from the time of the invention of firearms and the introduction of heavy artillery, stimulated the exploitation of iron and copper mines to a tremendous extent. . . .

. . . The development of exchange and of the war industry set the mining industry the following technical problems:

1. The raising of ores from considerable depths.
2. Methods of ventilating the mines.
3. The pumping out of water and water-conducting equipment, the problem of the pump.
4. The transfer from the crude, damp-blast method of production predominant until the 15th century, to the more perfect form of blast-furnace production, in which the problem of air-blast equipment is raised, as it is in ventilation also.
5. The working up of the ores with the aid of rolling and cutting machinery.

WAR AND WAR INDUSTRY

. . . Towards the end of the 17th century in all countries artillery lost its mediæval, craft character and was included as a component part of the army.

Consequently experiments on the inter-relationship of calibre and charge, the relationship of calibre to weight and length of barrel, on the phenomenon of recoil, developed on a large scale.

The progress of ballistics went hand in hand with the work of the most prominent of the physicists.

Galileo gave the world the theory of the parabolic trajectory of a ball; Torricelli, Newton, Bernoulli and Euler engaged in the investigation of the flight of a ball through the air, studied the resistance of the air and the causes of declination.

The development of artillery led in turn to a revolution in the construction of fortifications and fortresses, and this made enormous demands upon the engineering art.

The new form of defensive works (earth-work, fortresses) almost paralysed the activity of artillery in the middle of the 17th century, and this in turn gave a mighty impulse to its further development.

The development of the art of war raised the following technical problems:

INTRINSIC BALLISTICS

1. Study of the processes which occur in a firearm when fired and their improvement.
2. The stability combined with least weight of the firearm.
3. Adaptation to suitable and good aim.

EXTRINSIC BALLISTICS

4. The trajectory of a ball through a vacuum.
5. The trajectory of a ball through the air.
6. The dependence of air resistance upon the flight of the ball.
7. The deviation of a ball from its trajectory. . . .

THE PHYSICAL BASES OF THESE PROBLEMS

. . . Now let us systematically consider the problems of physics raised by the development of transport, industry and mining.

First and foremost we have to note that all of them are purely problems of mechanics.

We analyse in a very general way the basic themes of research in physics during the period in which merchant capital was becoming the predominant economic force and manufacture began to develop, i.e., the period from the beginning of the 16th to the second half of the 17th century.

We do not include Newton's works on physics, since they will be subjected to a special analysis. A comparison of the basic themes of physics enables us to determine the basic tendency of the interests of physics during the period immediately preceding Newton and contemporary with him.

1. The problem of simple machines, sloping surfaces and general problems of statics were studied by: Leonardo da Vinci (end of 16th century); Ubaldi (1577); Galileo (1589–1609); Cardan (middle of 16th century); and Stevin (1587).

2. The free fall of bodies and the trajectory of thrown bodies were studied by: Tartaglia (thirties of the 16th century); Benedetti (1587); Piccolomini (1598); Galileo (1589–1609); Riccioli (1652); The Academy del Cimente (1649).

3. The laws of hydro- and aerostatics, and atmospheric pressure. The pump, the movement of bodies through a resistant medium: Stevin, at the end of the 16th and beginning of the 17th centuries, the engineer and inspector of the land and water equipment of Holland; Galileo, Torricelli (first quarter of 17th century); Pascal (1647–1653); Herique (1650–1663), engineer to the army of Gustavus Adolphus, the builder of bridges and canals. Robert Boyle (seventies of the seventeenth century). Academy del Cimente (1657–1673).

4. Problems of the mechanics of the heavens, the theory of tides. Kepler (1609); Galileo (1609–1616); Gassendi (1647); Wren (sixties of 17th century); Halley (seventies of 17th century); Robert Hooke.

The above specified problems embrace almost the whole sphere of physics.

If we compare this basic series of themes with the physical problems which we found when analysing the technical demands of transport, means of communication, industry and war, it becomes quite clear that these problems of physics were fundamentally determined by these demands.

In fact the group of problems stated in the first paragraph constitute the physical problems relating to raising equipment and transmission mechanism important to the mining industry and the building art.

The second group of problems has fundamental significance for artillery and constitutes the basic physical tasks of ballistics.

The third group of problems is of fundamental importance to the problems of pumping water from mines and of their ventilation, the smelting of ores, the building of canals and locks, intrinsic ballistics and calculating the form of vessels.

The fourth group is of enormous importance to navigation. . . .

We have compared the main technical and physical problems of the period with the scheme of investigations governing physics during the period we are investigating, and we come to the conclusion that the scheme of physics was mainly determined by the economic and technical tasks which the rising bourgeoisie raised to the forefront.

During the period of merchant capital the development of productive forces set science a series of practical tasks and made an imperative demand for their accomplishment.

Official science, the centres of which were the mediæval universities, not only made no attempt to accomplish these tasks, but actively opposed the development of natural sciences. . . .

The struggle of the university and non-university science serving the needs of the rising bourgeoisie was a reflection in the ideological realm of the class struggle between the bourgeoisie and feudalism.

Science flourished step by step with the development and flourishing of the bourgeoisie. In order to develop its industry the bourgeoisie needed science, which would investigate the qualities of material bodies and the forms of manifestation of the forces of nature.

Hitherto science had been the humble servant of the church, and it was not allowed to pass beyond the bounds established by the church.

The bourgeoisie had need of science and science arose together with the bourgeoisie despite the church. (Engels.). . . .

We see that the rising bourgeoisie brought natural science into its service, the service of developing productive forces. At that time the most progressive class, it demanded the most progressive science. The English revolution gave a mighty stimulus to the development of productive forces. The necessity arose of not merely empirically resolving isolated problems, but of synthetically surveying and laying a stable theoretical basis for the solution by general methods of all the aggregate of physical problems, set for immediate solution by the development of the new technique.

And since (as we have already demonstrated) the basic complex of problems was that of mechanics this encyclopaedic survey of the physical problems was equivalent to the creation of a harmonious structure of theoretical mechanics which would supply general methods of resolving the tasks of the mechanics of earth and sky.

The explanation of this work fell to Newton to supply. The very name of his most important work indicates that Newton set himself this particular synthetic task.

In his introduction to the "Principia" Newton points out that applied mechanics and instruction on simple machinery had been worked out previously and that his task consisted not in "discussing the various *crafts* and in resolving sectional tasks, but in giving instruction on nature, the mathematical bases of physics."

Newton's "Principia" are expounded in abstract mathematical language and we should seek in them in vain for an exposition by Newton himself of the connection between the problems which he sets and solves with the technical demands out of which they arose.

Just as the geometrical method of exposition was not the method by means of which Newton made his discoveries, but, in his opinion, was to serve as a worthy vestment for the solutions found by other means, so in a work treating of "Natural philosophy" we cannot expect to find references to the "low" source of its inspiration.

We shall attempt to show that the "earthy core" of the "Principia" consists of just those technical problems which we have analysed above and which fundamentally determined the themes of physical research of the period.

Despite the abstract mathematical character of exposition adopted in the "Principia" Newton was not only not a learned scholastic divorced from life, but in the full sense of the word was in the centre of the physical and technical problems and interests of his time.

Newton's well-known letter to Francis Aston gives a very clear conception of his wide technical interests. The letter was written in 1669 after he had received his professorship, just as he was finishing the first outline of his theory of gravity.

Newton's young friend, Aston, was about to tour various countries of Europe, and he asked Newton to give him instructions how most rationally to utilise his journey and what especially was worthy of attention and study in the continental countries.

Briefly summarised, Newton's instructions were: diligently to study the mechanism of steering and the methods of navigating ships; attentively to survey all the fortresses he should happen to find, their method of construction, their powers of resistance, their advantages in defence, and in general to acquaint himself with war organisation. To study the natural riches of the country, especially the metals and minerals, and also to acquaint himself with the methods of their production and purification. To study the methods of obtaining metals from ores. To discover whether it was a fact that in Hungary, Slovakia and Bohemia close to the town of Eila or in the Bohemian mountains not far from Silesia there was a river with waters containing gold, also to ascertain whether the methods of obtaining gold from gold-bearing rivers by amalgamating with mercury remained a secret, or whether it was now generally known. In Holland a factory for polishing glass had recently been established; he must go to see it. He must learn how the Dutch protected their vessels from rot during their voyages to India. He must discover whether pendulum clocks were of any use in determining longitude during distant ocean expeditions. The methods of transforming one metal into another, iron into copper for instance, or of any metal into mercury, were especially worth attention and study. In Chemnitz and in Hungary, where there were gold and silver mines, it was said they knew how to transform iron into copper by dissolving the iron in vitriol, then boiling the solution, which on cooling yielded copper. Twenty years previously the acid possessing this noble property had been imported into England. Now it was not possible to obtain it. It was possible that they preferred to exploit it themselves in order to turn iron into copper to sell it. . . .

If we compare the circle of interests . . . briefly outlined above, we have no difficulty in noting that it embraces almost entirely all that group of problems which arose from the interests of transport, commerce, industry and military affairs during his period, which we summarised.

Now let us turn to an analysis of the contents of Newton's "Principia" and consider in what inter-relationships they stand with the themes of physical research of the period.

In the definitions and axioms or laws of motion are expounded the theoretical and methodo-logical bases of mechanics.

In the first book is a detailed exposition of the general laws of motion under the influence of central forces. In this way Newton provides a preliminary completion of the work to establish the general principles of mechanics which Galileo had begun.

Newton's laws provide a general method for the resolution of the great majority of mechanical tasks.

The second book, devoted to the problem of the movement of bodies, treats of a number of problems connected with the complex of problems which we have already noted.

The first three sections of the second book are devoted to the problem of the movement of bodies in a resistant medium in relation to various cases of the dependence of resistance upon speed (lineal resistance, resistance proportional to the second degree of speed and resistance proportional to part of the first part of the second degree).

As we have above shown when analysing the physical problems of ballistics, the development of which was connected with the development of heavy artillery, the tasks set and accomplished by Newton are of fundamental significance to extrinsic ballistics.

The fifth section of the second book is devoted to the fundamentals of hydrostatics and the problems of floating bodies. The same section considers the pressure of gases and the compression of gases and liquids under pressure.

When analysing the technical problems set by the construction of vessels, canals, water-pumping and ventilating equipment, we saw that the physical themes of these problems relate to the fundamentals of hydrostatics and aerostatics.

The sixth section deals with the problem of the movement of pendulums against resistance.

The laws governing the swing of mathematical and physical pendulums in a vacuum were found by Huygens in 1673 and applied by him to the construction of pendulum clocks.

We have seen from Newton's letter to Aston of what importance were pendulum clocks in determining longitude. The application of clocks in determining longitude led Huygens to the discovery of centrifugal force and the changes in acceleration of the force of gravity.

When the pendulum clocks brought by Richer from Paris to Caen in 1673 displayed a retarded movement Huygens was able at once to explain the phenomenon by the changes in acceleration of the force of gravity. The importance attached by Huygens himself to clocks is evident from the fact that his chief work is called: "On pendulum clocks."

Newton's works continue this course, and just as he passed from the mathematical case of the movement of bodies in a resistant medium with lineal resistance to the study of an actual case of movement, so he passed from the mathematical pendulum to an actual case of a pendulum's movement in a resistant medium.

The seventh section of the second book is devoted to the problem of movements of liquids and the resistance of a thrown body.

In it problems of hydrodynamics are considered, among them the problem of the efflux of liquids and the flow of water through tubes. As was above shown, all these problems are of cardinal importance in the construction and equipment of canals and locks and in planning water-pumping equipment.

In the same section the laws governing the fall of bodies through a resistant medium (water and air) are studied. As we know, these problems are of considerable importance in determining the trajectory of a thrown body and the trajectory of a shot.

The third book of the "Principia" is devoted to the "System of the World." It is devoted to the problems of the movements of planets, the movement of the moon and the anomalies of that movement, the acceleration of the force of gravity and its variations, in connection with the problem of the inequality of movement of chronometers in sea-voyages and the problem of tides. . . . [U]ntil the invention of the chronometer the movement of the moon was of fundamental importance in determining longitude. Newton returned to this problem more than once (in 1691). The study of the laws of the moon's movement was of fundamental importance in compiling exact tables for determining longitude, and the English "Council of Longitude" instituted a high reward for work on the moon's movement.

In 1713 Parliament passed a special bill to stimulate investigations in the sphere of determining longitude. Newton was one of the eminent members of the Parliamentary commission.

As we have pointed out in analysing the sixth section, the study of the movement of the pendulum, begun by Huygens, was of great importance to navigation consequently in the third book Newton studies the problem of the second pendulum, and subjects to analysis the movement of clocks during a number of ocean expeditions: that of Halley to St. Helena in 1677, Varenne's and de Hais's voyage to Martinique and Gaudeloupe in 1682, Couple's journey to Lisbon, etc., in 1697, and a voyage to America in 1700.

When analysing the causes of tides Newton subjects the height of flow tides in various ports and river mouths to analysis, and discusses the problem of the height of flows in dependence on the local situation of the port and the forms of the flow.

This rough outline of the contents of the "Principia" exhibits the complete coincidence of the physical thematics of the period, which arose out of the needs of economics and technique, with the main contents of the "Principia," which in the full sense of the word is a survey and systematic resolution of all the main group of physical problems. And as by their character all these problems were problems of mechanics, it is clear that Newton's chief work was a survey of the mechanics of the earth and the heavenly bodies.

SCIENCE, TECHNOLOGY AND SOCIETY IN SEVENTEENTH CENTURY ENGLAND

ROBERT K. MERTON

America's leading sociologist, Robert K. Merton (1910–   ), is also her most prominent exponent of the sociology of science. Merton received his graduate training at Harvard University, where he worked with sociologists Pitirim A. Sorokin and Talcott Parsons, and with the distinguished historian of science, George Sarton. While at Harvard he completed his lengthy and influential study of science, technology, and religion in seventeenth-century England. The fact that this monograph is, after three decades, still an outstanding work in the sociology of science is both an indication of Merton's superior abilities and the lack of scholarly interest in this branch of sociological research. Merton had clearly shown that the analytical and historical techniques available to the sociologist could be used effectively to investigate science as a social institution. Few, however, chose to follow the path he opened. The sociology of science remains one of the minor areas of specialty within sociology. In the meantime, Merton's own interests had shifted from the sociology of science to sociological theory and other problems in sociology (professionalization, mass communications). Recently he has turned once again to some central issues in the sociology of science: priority disputes among scientists and the meaning of multiple discoveries in science.

Merton is Professor of Sociology at Columbia University and a past president of the American Sociological Association.

RELIGION IS ONE EXPRESSION of cultural values — and in the seventeenth century a clearly dominating expression. In view of this, the commonly accepted and even more widely discussed thesis that science and religion have always been at odds is not unrelated to our inquiry. In the nineteenth century, bold intellectuals berated religious opposition and saw in the outcome of this conflict the triumph of reason over superstition, whereas pacific mediators sought to establish an essential harmony between science and religion. Neither of these was a properly sociological point of view. The sociologist is not a Defender of the Faith, religious or scientific. When he has uncovered the sentiments crystallized in religious values and the cultural orientation which governs their expression, when he has determined the extent to which this led men toward or away from scientific pursuits or perhaps influenced them not at all, then his task is, in its initial outlines, complete.

Puritanism, evoking and shaping the sentiments which pervaded every phase of human action in this period, was the religious movement which notably incorporated dominant cultural values. As such, it provided a measuring rod for the worth of various social activities. What, then, were its relations to science? Did Puritanism, as so often we are told, involve that sort of fervid fanaticism which brooks nothing but its own religious goals? And, if so, what of the cultural implications of

From Robert K. Merton, "Science, Technology and Society in Seventeenth Century England," *Osiris*, Vol. IV (1938), pp. 414–565. Reprinted by permission of *Osiris* and of the author.

39

such an attitude? What were the consequences for the new science of the powerful motivations which derived from Puritanism? In short, we are concerned with the complex modes of interaction between a religious ethic and science, not as these appear to apologists of the two camps, but as they occurred in the course of actual social development. . . .

The Protestant Ethic

. . . The conception of "meritory works" was of course . . . current in the Middle Ages, but — especially in the early part of that epoch — its meaning was radically different from that of the Protestant precept. Monastic limitations and an other-worldly orientation (in a quite different sense from that of the Calvinists) were insuperable barriers to the utilization of the concept in active, worldly service. For both medieval Catholicism and Calvinism, this world was evil, but, whereas the prescribed solution for the one was retirement from the world into the spiritual calm of the monastery, it was incumbent on the other to conquer the temptations of this world by *remaking it* through ceaseless, unflinching toil. The sentiments with which the various Puritan sects were imbued, despite different rationalizations and theological views, led to approximately identical implications for social conduct. . . .

As we shall see, the mode of life which bore the imprint of Calvinism was not so much adherence to the logical implications of a system of theology as domination by a particular group of sentiments. The values implicit in these doctrines which struck the deepest roots in English life were those congenial to tendencies developing independently in other compartments of culture, and, in this way, Puritanism was integrated with many cultural trends which were in their incipiency. A number of studies have shown that the Protestant ethos exerted a stimulative effect upon capitalism. Since science and technology play such dominant rôles in modern capitalistic culture, it is possible that tangible relationships likewise exist between the development of science and Puritanism. Indeed Max Weber incidentally notes the possibility of such a connection. . . .

The social values inherent in the Puritan ethos were such as to lead to an approbation of science because of a basically utilitarian orientation, couched in religious terms and furthered by religious authority. Scientific investigation, viewed from the rationalized Puritan system of ethics, seemed to possess those qualities characteristic of activities which are effective means for the attainment of the accepted goals. The possibility that science, as a means toward a religious end, would later break away from such religious supports and in a measure tend to delimit the realm of theologic control, was seemingly unrealized. The apparent conflicts between theology and science which arose when scientific findings seemed to disprove various contentions of orthodox theologians occurred later with each extension of scientific inquiry to realms which were hitherto regarded as "sacred." But this is simply another example of the frequently observed fact that the Reformers did not anticipate the full actual consequences of their teachings, consequences which did not coincide with their expectations.

V. MOTIVE FORCES OF THE NEW SCIENCE

Puritanism attests to the theorem that non-logical notions with a transcendental reference may nevertheless exercise a considerable influence upon practical behavior. If the fancies of an inscrutable deity do not lend themselves to scientific investigation, human action predicated upon a particular concept of this deity does. It was precisely Puritanism which built a new bridge between the transcendental and human action, thus supplying a motive force for the new science. To be sure, Puritan doctrines rested ultimately upon an esoteric theological base but these were translated into the familiar and cogent language of the laity.

To the "Glory of the Great Author of Nature"

. . . The Protestant ethic had pervaded the realm of science and had left its indelible stamp upon the attitude of scientists toward their work. Expressing his motives, anticipating possible objections, facing actual censure, the scientist found motive, sanction and authority alike in the Puritan teachings. Such a dominant force as religion in those days was not, and perhaps could not, be compartmentalized and delimited. Thus in Boyle's highly-commended apologia of science, we read:

. . . it will be no venture to suppose that at least in the Creating of the Sublunary World, and the more conspicuous Stars, two of God's principal ends were, the Manifestation of His own Glory, and the Good of Men. . . .

This is the motif which recurs in constant measure in the very writings which often contain considerable scientific contributions: these worldly activities and scientific achievements manifest the Glory of God and enhance the Good of Man. The juxtaposition of the spiritual and the material is characteristic and significant. This culture rested securely on a substratum of utilitarian norms which identified the useful and the true. Puritanism itself had imputed a threefold utility to science. Natural philosophy was instrumental first, in establishing practical proofs of the scientist's state of grace; second, in enlarging control of nature and third, in glorifying God. Science was enlisted in the service of individual, society and deity. That these were adequate grounds could not be denied. They comprised not merely a claim to legitimacy, they afforded incentives which can not be readily overestimated. . . .

Rationalism and Empiricism

The exaltation of the faculty of reason in the Puritan ethos — based partly on the conception of rationality as a curbing device of the passions — inevitably led to a sympathetic attitude toward those activities which demand the constant application of rigorous reasoning. But again, in contrast to medieval rationalism, reason is deemed subservient and auxiliary to empiricism. . . . It is on this point probably that Puritanism and the scientific temper are in most salient agreement, for the combination of rationalism and empiricism which is so pronounced in the Puritan ethic forms the essence of the spirit of modern science.

The Puritan insistence upon empiricism, upon the experimental approach, was intimately connected with the identification of contemplation with idleness, of the expenditure of physical energy and the handling of material objects with industry. Experiment was the scientific expression of the practical, active and methodical bents of the Puritan. This is not to say, of course, that experiment was derived in any sense from Puritanism. But it serves to account for the ardent support of the new experimental science by those who had their eyes turned toward the other world and their feet firmly planted on this. . . .

The Shift to Science

As the full import of the Puritan ethic manifested itself — even after the political failure of the Revolution which should not be erroneously identified with the collapse of Puritan influence upon social attitudes — the sciences became foci of social interest. Their new fashionableness contrasts with their previous state of comparative obscurity. This was not without its effects. Many, who hitherto might have turned to theology or rhetoric or philology, were directed, through the subtle, largely unperceived and newly-arisen predisposition of society, into scientific channels. . . .

The science-loving amateur, so prominent a feature of the latter part of the century, is . . . evidence of the effect of this new attitude. Nobles and wealthy commoners turned to science, not as a means of livelihood, but as an object of devoted interest. Particularly for these individuals were direct utilitarian benefits of an economic nature a wholly negligible consideration. Science afforded them an opportunity of devoting their energies to a highly honored task; an imperative duty as the comforts of unrelieved idleness vanished from the new scale of values. . . .

The Process of Secularization

The beginnings of . . . secularization, faintly perceptible in the latter Middle Ages, were, in one sense, emerging more fully in the Puritan ethos. But the Puritan was not simply the last of the medievalists or the first of the moderns. He was both. It was in the system of Puritan values, as we have seen, that reason and experience began to be considered as independent means of ascertaining even religious truth. Faith which is unquestioning and not "rationally weighed," proclaimed Baxter, is not faith, but a dream or fancy or opinion. In effect this grants to science a power which may ultimately limit that of religion. This unhesitant assignment of a virtual hegemony to science is based on the explicit assumption of the unity of knowledge, experiential and supersensuous, so that the testimony of science must perforce corroborate religious convictions. . . .

The Integration of Religion and Science

It is thus to the religious ethos, not the theology, that we must turn if we are to understand the integration of science and religion in seventeenth century England.

Perhaps the most directly effective belief in this ethos for the sanction of natural science held that the study of nature enables a fuller appreciation of His works and thus leads us to admire and praise the Power, Wisdom and Goodness of God manifested in His creation. Though this conception was not unknown to medieval thinkers, the consequences deduced from it were entirely different. For example, Arnaldus of Villanova, in studying the products of the Divine Workshop, adheres strictly to the medieval scholastic ideal of determining the properties of phenomena from *tables* (in which, according to the canons of logic, all combinations of chance

were set forth). But in the seventeenth century, the contemporary emphasis upon empiricism led to the investigation of nature primarily through experience. This difference in interpretation of substantially the same doctrine can only be understood in the light of the different values permeating the two cultures. Cloistered contemplation was forsaken; active experimentation was introduced.

Community of Tacit Assumptions in Science and Puritanism

Up to this point we have been concerned, in the main, with the directly felt sanction of science by the Protestant ethic. Now, while this was of great importance, there was still another relationship which, subtle and difficult of apprehension though it be, was perhaps of equal significance. Puritanism was one element in the preparation of a set of largely implicit assumptions which made for the ready acceptance of the characteristic scientific temper of the seventeenth and subsequent centuries. It is not simply that Protestantism promoted free inquiry, *libre examen,* or decried monastic asceticism. These oft-mentioned characteristics touch only the bare surface of the relationship.

It has become manifest that in each age there is a system of science which rests upon a set of assumptions, usually implicit and seldom, if ever, questioned by most of the scientific workers of the time. The basic assumption in modern science, that is in the type of scientific work which becoming pronounced in the seventeenth century has since continued, "is a widespread, instinctive conviction in the existence of an *Order of Things,* and, in particular, of an Order of Nature.". . .

But this conviction, prerequisite condition of modern science though it is, was not sufficient to induce its development. What was needed was a constant interest in searching for this order of nature in an empirical and rational fashion, *i.e.,* an *active interest* in this world and in its occurrences plus a specifically empirical ap proach. With Protestantism religion provided this interest — it actually imposed obligations of intense concentration on secular activity with an emphasis on experience and reason as bases for action and belief. . . .

VI. PURITANISM, PIETISM AND SCIENCE: TESTING AN HYPOTHESIS

. . . Puritanism, and ascetic Protestantism generally, emerges as an emotionally consistent system of beliefs, sentiments and action which played no small part in arousing a sustained interest in science. To use the word "education" in its primitive sense, we may say that Puritanism was a basic component of the scientific education of this period. Patently, this is not to deny the importance of a host of other factors — economic, political, and above all the self-fertilizing movement of science itself — which served to swell the rising scientific current. No doubt, too, these associated factors outweighed the religious component in certain historical situations. The burgeoning of science in sixteenth century Italy testifies to this. But the rise of science which antedated the Reformation or developed quite independently of it does not negate the significance of ascetic Protestantism in this respect. Rather, it attests that other circumstances may equally conduce to the espousal of science and that these factors may be sufficiently effective to overcome the antagonism involved in the existing religious system.

Furthermore, if for the purposes of investigation, the relations between Puritanism and science have been isolated from a wider social context, the concrete importance of this context is not thereby denied. It may well be argued that ascetic Protestantism itself is the product of more pervasive cultural changes. In this research, however, we are not concerned with such far-reaching questions. In any case, it is evident that the formal organization of values constituted by Puritanism led to the largely unwitting furtherance of modern science. The Puritan complex of a scarcely

distinguished utilitarianism; of intramundane interests; methodical, unremitting action; thoroughgoing empiricism; of the right and even the duty of *libre examen;* of anti-traditionalism — all this was congenial to the same values in science. The happy marriage of these two movements was based on an intrinsic compatibility and even in the nineteenth century, their divorce was not yet final.

VII. SCIENCE, TECHNOLOGY AND ECONOMIC DEVELOPMENT: MINING

. . . [W]e have considered the relations between certain changes in the value system, particularly as expressed in Puritanism, and the growth of interest in science and technology. A parallel has been suggested between the norms governing the activities of the Puritan and of the scientist. But if this congeniality of the Puritan and the scientific temper partly explains the increased tempo of scientific activity during the later seventeenth century, by no means does it account for the particular foci of scientific and technologic investigation. Which forces guided the interests of scientists and inventors into particular channels? Was the choice of problems a wholly personal concern, completely unrelated to the socio-cultural background? Or was this selection significantly limited and guided by social forces? If so, what was the extent of this influence? . . .

The Growth of Mining

However engrossed he may have been in his work, the seventeenth century scientist could scarcely remain oblivious to the profound economic growth of his time. There occurred a striking change in the scale and amplitude of economic enterprise. Capitalism, well-defined, widely-extended, is moving in. The once popular view that capitalistic enterprise first followed upon the largely apocryphal Industrial Revolution is now properly discredited. In closer accord with the facts is the view that at least the extractive industries, the textile manufacture and the metal trades of the seventeenth century all exhibited, in varying degree, the characteristics of capitalism. The growth of markets and a pronounced division of labor became associated with the markedly increased incidence of capitalistic undertakings, of large-scale production, to such a degree, that this change may well be compared to that which occurred toward the close of the eighteenth century.

Associated with the inroads of capitalism is a complex of interests, wants and activities, a far-reaching process of rationalization, and an application of scientific and empirical technical knowledge to industrial processes. It is hardly an historical accident that the last year of the sixteenth century saw not only the publication of Gilbert's *De Magnete*, the first important scientific work produced in England and the augury of the new era of science, but also the chartering of the East India Company, the first English joint-stock company of importance and herald of the forthcoming bourgeois age.

Foremost among the economic enterprises of this period rank the extractive industries — the mining of coal, iron, tin, and copper — and textile industries. . . .

Modes of Economic Influence

It would seem, then, that a certain proportion of theoretical "pure" science is directly concerned with problems which derive from practical exigencies. It also sets up derivative studies which are related only in a very indirect fashion to the immediate problems of technique. In this connection, however, it is important to distinguish the subjective attitudes of individual scientists from the social rôle played by their research. Clearly, many scientists of this period viewed their works as an "end-in-itself"; they were sufficiently enamoured of their subject to pursue it for its own sake, with no consideration of the immediate practical significance of their investigations. Nor is there any implication that all individual researches are necessarily linked to technical tasks. The significant point is that much of the scientific research of this

period was oriented — not always with deliberate intent on the part of the scientist — toward subjects which were profoundly useful for technical development; subjects which because of the social and economic emphasis of the period came to the attention of scientists as worthy of further study.

Thus the relation between science and economic needs is seen to be twofold: direct, in the sense that certain scientific research is advisedly and deliberately pursued for utilitarian ends, and indirect, in so far as certain subjects, because of their technologic importance, are sufficiently emphasized to be selected for study though the scientists are not necessarily cognizant of their practical significance. . . .

VIII. SCIENCE, TECHNOLOGY AND ECONOMIC DEVELOPMENT: TRANSPORTATION

One notable aspect of the economic expansion of this period was the need for more adequate means of transportation and communication. The growth of the coal trade particularly evoked the growth of the merchant marine, since water-transport was so much cheaper than that by land. Foreign trade had first reached considerable proportions in England in the second half of the sixteenth century. St. Helena, Jamaica, the East American coast, were but the beginnings of England's great colonial expansion. The growth of internal trade also enhanced the need for improved facilities for land and river transport: proposals for turnpikes and canals were common in the seventeenth century.

Growth of Transportation

. . . In general, . . . it may be said that the contemporary scientists, ranging from the indefatigable virtuoso Petty to the nonpareil Newton, definitely focussed their attention upon technical tasks made prominent by problems of navigation and upon derivative scientific research. The latter category, however, needs careful delimitation. While it is true that a congeries of scientific investigation may be traced to technical demands, it is equally evident that much of this research can be understood as a logical development of foregoing scientific advance. It is only because the scientists themselves point to the practical implications of their work that one becomes inclined to accept the appreciable directive influence of practical problems. Even that "purest" of disciplines, mathematics, held little interest for Newton save as it was designed for application to physical problems.

Some attention was likewise paid to inland transportation although to a less extent than to maritime transport, possibly because of the greater economic significance of the latter. The growing interior traffic demanded considerable improvement. . . . Characteristically, contemporary scientists . . . sought to overcome technical difficulties. . . . These efforts evidence the attempts of scientists to contribute technological props to business enterprise; these particular instances being devoted to making possible the extension of markets, one of the primary characteristics of capitalism.

IX. SCIENCE AND MILITARY TECHNIQUE

It was not until the seventeenth century that England attained its position of military and commercial leadership. Frequent recourse to force of arms attended this rise to power. Not only were there fifty-five years of actual warfare during this century, but also the greatest revolution in English history. Coincident with this prolonged warfare occurred a number of changes in military technique. The dominance of firearms — both muskets and artillery — over side-arms first became marked at this time. The period represents a turning-point in the history of armaments: swords and pikes disappeared almost completely as weapons of importance (save as they are incorporated in the removable bayonet about 1680) and firearms were used almost exclusively. Especially notable was the enhanced use of heavy artillery, for in this field occurred a change of scale which raised or emphasized many new technical problems. . . .

. . . [I]t seems probable that the needs generated by military technology influenced the foci of scientific interests to an appreciable degree.

But the extent of this influence is still problematical. It is by no means certain that much the same distribution of interests would not have occurred, irrespective of this external pressure. Many of these problems likewise flowed directly from the intrinsic developments of science. It may be argued that the disinterested search for truth coupled with the logical concatenation of scientific problems is sufficient to account for the particular direction of research. In point of fact, however, a cumulating body of evidence leads to the conclusion that *some* rôle must be accorded these factors external to science, properly so-called. The following chapter is devoted to the effort to determine, as precisely as possible (although we can at best hope for only a very crude estimate), the extent to which military, economic and technical influences were operative.

X. EXTRINSIC INFLUENCES ON SCIENTIFIC RESEARCH

The question of the relative importance of intrinsic and external factors in the determination of the foci of scientific interest has long been debated. One camp of theorists has pledged itself to the conviction that science has virtually no autonomy of its own. The direction of scientific advance is held to be almost exclusively the outcome of external, particularly of economic, pressure. Joining issue with these extremists are others who argue that the pure scientist is shut off from the social world in which he lives and that his subjects of research are determined by the strict necessity which inheres in each logic-tight compartment of science. Each of these points of view is justified by an appeal to carefully selected cases which nominally bear out one or the other of these conflicting opinions.

In a recently published lecture, Dr. Sarton mediates between these views and poses the problem in respect to mathematics as follows:

There is no doubt that mathematical discoveries are conditioned by outside events of every kind, political, economic, scientific, military, and by the incessant demands of the arts of peace and war. Mathematics did never develop in a political or economic vacuum. However, we think that those events were only some of the factors among others, factors the power of which might vary and did vary from time to time. It might be almost decisive in one case, and ineffectual in another.

Mutatis mutandis, the same might be said of science generally. Of especial importance is the suggestion that the influence of these extrinsic conditioning factors is not constant for this implies that we cannot extend our findings for the seventeenth century without further ado to the history of science in general. But this does not preclude a systematic examination of the extent to which such factors pervaded scientific research during the latter part of the seventeenth century.

A Statement of Procedure

The minutes of the Society as transcribed in Birch's *History of the Royal Society* provide one basis for such a study. A feasible, though in many ways inadequate, procedure consists of a classification and tabulation of the researches discussed at these meetings, together with an examination of the context in which the various problems came to light. This should afford some grounds for deciding roughly the extent to which extrinsic factors operated directly or indirectly.

Since Birch's transcription extends only through the meetings of 1687, this provides one temporal limit of our study. Meetings during the four years 1661, 1662, 1686 and 1687 are considered. . . .

Summary of Results

From this tabulation it appears that less than half (41.3%) of the various investigations conducted during the four years in hand were devoted to pure science. If we add to this the items which were only indirectly related to practical needs (7.4% to marine transport, 17.5% to mining, and 3.6% to military techniques), then about seventy percent of this research had no practical affiliations. Since these figures are but grossly approximate, the results may be summarized by saying that from forty to seventy percent was in the category of pure science; and conversely that from thirty to sixty percent was influenced by practical requirements.

Again, considering only the research *directly* related to practical needs, it appears that problems of marine transport attracted the most attention. This is not surprising since the contemporary scientists were well aware of the problems raised by England's insular position — problems both military and commercial in nature — and were eager to rectify them. Of almost equal importance was the influence of military technique. . . .

Likewise, mining which developed so markedly in seventeenth century England, had an appreciable influence upon the selection of subjects for scientific analysis. In this instance, the greater part of scientific, as distinct from technologic, research was in the fields of mineralogy and metallurgy with the aim of discovering new utilizable ores and new methods of extracting metals from the ore.

It is interesting to note that in the latter years considered in this summary, there was an increasing proportion of investigation in the field of pure science. This may be accounted for in several ways. First, it is possible that at the outset the members of the Society were anxious to justify their activities (to the Crown and the general public) by deriving practical results as soon as possible. Hence they would be apt to concentrate their attention upon investigations which would be most apt to lead to such useful effects. Furthermore, many of the problems which were at first advisedly investigated because of their practical importance may be later studied with no awareness of their practical implications. In these instances, though it would not be an exaggeration to ascribe the choice of these subjects to practical urgencies, it is impossible to determine whether they aroused attention because of their intrinsic scientific interest or because of their ultimate utility. It would be a matter of dubious inference to denote these as influenced by socio-economic needs and hence they were, more or less arbitrarily, classified as "pure science." Therefore, the results, if they are at all biassed, are weighted on the side of pure science.

On the basis of the data presented in the last three chapters it may be tentatively maintained that socio-economic needs influenced considerably the selection of subjects of investigation by scientists in seventeenth century England. Speaking roughly, about thirty to sixty percent of the contemporary researches seem, directly or indirectly, to have been so influenced.

THE SCIENTIFIC ROLE:
The Conditions of
Its Establishment in Europe

JOSEPH BEN-DAVID

The Israeli sociologist Joseph Ben-David (1920–   ) has made comparative sociological studies of productivity and innovation in science during the nineteenth century and of the role of the universities in modern societies. He is the author of a survey entitled the Professions in the Class System of Present-Day Societies (Current Sociology, XIII, 3, 1963–64) and is currently engaged in writing a book on the sociology of science. An excerpt from this forthcoming volume is reprinted here.

Ben-David is Associate Professor of Sociology at the Hebrew University in Jerusalem. He is a former fellow of the Center for Advanced Study in the Behavioral Sciences, Stanford, California (1957–58) and he served as Visiting Professor of Sociology at the University of California, Berkeley (1964–65).

INTRODUCTORY REMARKS

ANCIENT SCIENCE FAILED to develop not because of its immanent shortcomings but because those who did scientific work did not see themselves, nor were they seen by others, as scientists, but primarily as philosophers, medical practitioners, or astrologers. Only this can explain why the appearance of Galileo had to wait for some 1,800 years after Archimedes, or the even longer gap between Aristotle's and Theophrastus' systematisations of living and growing things and those of Linnaeus and Cuvier. Had there existed among the Greeks several generations of intellectuals conceiving of themselves as scientists — with the motivations and obligations entailed in that — they could undoubtedly have ap-

From Joseph Ben-David, "The Scientific Role: The Conditions of Its Establishment in Europe," Minerva (Autumn, 1965), pp. 15–50. Reprinted by permission of Minerva and of the author.

plied themselves to the discovery of a less cumbersome method of mathematical notation and have made many of the scientific advances accomplished in the sixteenth and seventeenth centuries and subsequently. It is true that much of the Greek tradition was lost in the Middle Ages as a result of catastrophes but the stagnation and deterioration of the tradition had started earlier. Furthermore, had there been a group of persons, who inherited the Greek scientific tradition and who regarded themselves as scientists, anywhere in the Christian or the Moslem world or among the Jews, the Greek achievements might have been rediscovered in the Middle Ages or, at any rate, much more efficient use would have been made of them in the fifteenth century.

The question, therefore, is what made certain men in seventeenth-century Europe, and nowhere before, view themselves as scientists and see the scientific role as one with unique and special obligations and possibilities. The general conditions necessary for this occurrence were: either there had to be some striking scientific discoveries of practical value convincing people that the practice of science was an economically worthwhile occupation, or there had to be a group of persons who believed in science as an intrinsically valuable preoccupation and who had a reasonable prospect of making their belief generally accepted, even before science proved its economic worth. In what follows I will first sketch in outline the main steps of this development. Then I will present each step in detail.

STAGES IN THE FORMATION OF AN AUTONOMOUS SCIENTIFIC ROLE

Traditionally, natural science was subordinated to theology and philosophy. A first step towards the modern efflorescence occurred when it began to become more differentiated from theology and philosophy with respect to its subject-matter and procedures. Even when this point was reached, science continued to be a peripheral and secondary interest, but once its continuity was assured by its patent singularity and the steadiness of the concern which it attracted, it ceased to be subject to intermittent deterioration and there was even a probability of some slow but regular accumulation of scientific knowledge. The next step occurred when this peripheral subject, which had had a low status, relative to other intellectual fields, came to be regarded by groups, with class, religious and political interests opposed to the established order, as intellectually more meaningful to them than the existing theological, philosophical and literary culture. For these groups, the sciences became a central part of their culture. Under these circumstances, men interested in science were impelled to redefine their roles as philosophers in such a way that science became increasingly central instead of peripheral to their conception of what they were doing. With the enhancement of the wealth, power and status of the classes which adopted an outlook sympathetic to science and in opposition to the inherited outlook, the status of the new type of philosopher was elevated. With the advancement of the status of scientific activity, the numbers of intellectuals of the highest quality moving into the field increased. The final steps occurred in the seventeenth century when the political success of the classes adopting the scientistic outlook, combined with the intellectual success of the new philosophers, led to a more elaborate organisation of science and the establishment of scientific journals. In the course of these developments, men who did scientific work came to regard themselves and to be regarded by others as different from philosophers. They came to regard themselves as carrying on a significantly distinctive category of activity, disjunctively separated from the intellectual activity of philosophers and theologians. Increasing in numbers and having more occasion to meet and discuss with each other, they developed their own culture, their own norms and traditions in which their scientific work was embedded. The motivation and curiosity sustained by the stabilised stimulus inherent in such intensified and persistent scientific activity made for a greater continuity in scientific development. With a larger number of persons convinced of the value of science and devoting themselves actively and fully to its cultivation, science became, in a sense, a self-perpetuating domain of culture, and more independent than before of the variations in its environment.

A further contributory factor was the relative openness and decentralisation of the social system of European intellectual life. The Continent, including England, constituted a cultural whole, as a result of the unity of the church and its adoption of Roman traditions; persons and writings travelled across political borders with relative ease. Ideas evolved in one place would be readily appreciated in another. At the same time the various political units were sufficiently different from each other to permit beginnings, which were constricted in their places of origin (because they clashed with important vested interests), to be developed elsewhere, where the same vested interests were for some reason weaker.

* * *

THE PERIPHERALITY OF SCIENCE IN THE MEDIEVAL UNIVERSITY

Since geometry and dynamics were mainly cultivated by philosophers, the fate of these studies was (up to the sixteenth century) bound up with that of the philosophical studies in general. The tradition of medieval natural science was started at Oxford by masters of Merton College. From there it spread to Paris, which had the closest intellectual commerce with Oxford. When the tradition declined in both places during the fourteenth century, as did philosophy, the centre shifted to Italy, mainly to Padua, and to the new German, Dutch and other universities. Thus, when, in the fourteenth and fifteenth centuries, special university chairs were established, this tradition, influenced probably by inter-

nal developments within the medical faculty, also led to the establishment of professorships in mathematics, astronomy, and a variety of subjects, such as natural philosophy. Aristotelian physics, etc., first in Italy and later everywhere in Europe. These scientific chairs were of subordinate importance; it was an advancement for their incumbents if they could be appointed as professors of philosophy, or even better, of theology, law or medicine. It was in any case necessary to have a degree in these latter subjects in order to be appointed to a chair. Nevertheless, the natural sciences were, by this time, more or less regularly taught — on however modest a level — by professors who were paid for teaching them. . . .

Thus although mathematics and some natural science were taught with sufficient frequency to produce a supply of potential scientists, they were not taught with enough concentration to create in a small number of persons an image of themselves as scientists. Science was a marginal activity within the university and those who learned it there saw their knowledge of it as a peripheral feature in the image they had of themselves. Those who studied science at universities did not acquire enough of it for them to form a strong attachment to it. There were not enough other persons in university circles, interaction with whom could intensify their own interest in science, which was otherwise insufficiently strong to live entirely from their own individual inner motivation. Finally it was evident that science was held in fairly low esteem by the authorities of church, state and university. For the incentive to do science wholeheartedly, all three of these conditions would have to change.

ARTISTS AND "SCIENTISTS" IN ITALY: THE RUDIMENTARY FORMATION OF THE SCIENTIFIC ROLE

The first signs of a change in the evaluation of science appear in the circles of artists and engineers in fifteenth-century Italy. Till then, artists were considered mere artisans but, as a result of the general conditions which made possible a modicum of autonomy for various urban groups, . . . their fortunes were improving in the fifteenth century.

In addition to the new interest in art, this improvement was perhaps even more closely related to the fact that the role of artist often overlapped, in the same person, with the roles of architect, fortification engineer and ballistic expert. . . .

The artists had certain "status problems" in common with scientists. The artists and technologists had hitherto been relatively low in their position in society. The only practical way to assert the status of their calling and to prove the spiritual value of what had been traditionally considered as a lowly manual art was through giving evidence of the connection between their work and a recognised scholarly pursuit. They were, however, little interested in the acquisition of classical languages and had no sense for philosophical speculation. The only scholars with whom they had a common interest were those cultivating the sciences.

This gradually changed the self-image of the scientifically-inclined scholar. In the university community on which his status had up till then depended entirely, his interests were considered as of merely peripheral importance. If he wanted to obtain recognition, he had to prove his worth in the more central fields of scholarship. Now, however, there was an upcoming profession, that of the artists, for whom philosophy was first and foremost science. Viewing themselves through the eyes of these new clients or public, who appreciated what they had to offer, the scientist-scholars gained self-confidence. There was a basis here for viewing science and mathematics as the centre of a new philosophy still to be created. . . . As a result there developed a continuous interchange between artists and "scientists" lasting throughout the fifteenth century. . . .

The hybrid identity of artist-scientist was a transient phenomenon. By the beginning of the sixteenth century, the painters and architects had learned everything that could be useful to them in geometry and optics, which was not a great deal. With Michelangelo there set in a reaction against the confusion of art with science. . . . By the middle of the sixteenth century the relationship between science and art reverted to the earlier pattern of two endeavours running widely separate courses and having few meaningful encounters. To the extent that there was continued contact, there was nothing in it to introduce a new element in the situation. It was only the development into a routine of something which in the previous century had been a revelation.

Meanwhile, in the northern countries of Europe there emerged, starting from the 1530s, a growing trend towards extolling the virtues of arts and crafts and the knowledge of nature. This began in the writings of Ludovico Vives, Erasmus, Montaigne and Rabelais and can be traced through Palissy to Bacon's new philosophy. This intellectual trend ran hand in hand with the continued growth in the social importance of new classes whose outlook was sympathetic neither with the scholastic nor the humanistic intellectual establishments. In Italy, on the other hand, artists and technologists had been — in spite of attempts in this direction — unable to break away from the domination of the guilds. The scientists as well as the small number of very eminent artists were now moving in a quite different, upper class, humanistic environment — the environment of the academies. . . . Thus at a time when the Northern European class structure became increasingly fluid and a mobile "middle" class was increasing in size, in awareness of itself and in self-sufficiency, the Italian class structure recrystallised into something approximating its earlier form.

THE RECONQUEST OF SCIENCE BY THE NON-SCIENTIFIC CULTURE IN ITALY

For our purpose, the main point is that in other parts of Europe the cause of science was taken up by a class of persons who stood to gain from certain changes in the social order. In Italy by contrast, science became, by the sixteenth century, the concern of a minority within a class which had attained what it wanted and which was interested in the stability of the social order.

After their interlude among the artists, the Italian scientists began to feel strong enough to seek the recognition of the official intellectual community. This was eventually denied them by the ruling circles of the church and the state, as well as the intellectual establishment. In this process of overture and rejection, so essential to an understanding of the stagnation of Italian science, the Italian academies played a great part. . . .

The first century of the academies may be interpreted as essentially an attempt of persons, many of whom otherwise might have been forced to work through established university faculties of arts, to create for themselves an intellectually more congenial institution than the universities provided. They did so by making use of the new resources of wealth and protection in such centres as Florence, Rome, Naples and, later, Paris and London. The numbers of persons with such interests were increasing; many of them did not have to gain their livelihood from teaching. They sought to enrich their understanding by each other's company in which they discussed things of common interest. . . .

For the first century of their existence, each academy tended to embrace almost the entire range of intellectual activities. After the middle of the sixteenth century, general academies with a wide diversity of purposes were founded with less frequency. Specialised academies started springing up, of which half or more were literary academies, the rest being divided between theatrical, legal, medical, theological, scientific, and artistic purposes. . . . There was also a significant change in their social structure. Instead of being relatively informal groups, they became increasingly formal institutions, conferring upon their members publicly recognised honours. Among other things, this was manifested in the composition of the membership in which noble amateurs tended to outnumber the professional intellectuals. This tendency toward formalisation occurred in the literary and multipurpose academies in the middle and the end of the century but in the scientific academies only at the end of the seventeenth and in the eighteenth centuries. . . .

The academies provided a flexible framework for the expression of the cultural interests of different groups of intellectuals where those interests could not be fulfilled by existing institutions. The existence of such institutions in Italy as a means of coping with newly emerged interests would seem to indicate the relative openness of Italian social structure, as compared with the rest of Europe, where academies were only created in imitation of the Italian models.

As a matter of fact, however, what appears as openness is better interpreted as evidence of rigidity. A price had to be paid for the relatively easy absorption of the leading merchants into the nobility and for the relative ease with which the new cultural pursuits were accommodated within academies, and the academies within the official hierarchy of cultural institutions. The price which had to be paid was the assumption of the habits of thought, attitudes and style of the upper classes, to the point where the spirit of innovation eventually expired.

One of the results was the abandonment of the practical concerns of science. Whereas in England and in France, propaganda for the official recognition of science was based on its potential usefulness to technology and production, in Italy its claims were justified by arguments from Platonic philosophy or neo-Platonic mysticism. The cause of science in Northern Europe was supported, not only by certain, usually upper class, intellectual circles actually cultivating it but by a considerable element of merchants, artisans and seafarers. In Italy it was espoused only by an

upper class intellectual clique trying to dis-
place the official university philosophers
and modernise the intellectual outlook of
the Catholic church. . . .

The picture, therefore, is not one of a
movement gaining wider and wider support and then violently suppressed but
rather of an episode well contained within
an established intellectual fraternity which
was decaying. By the end of the seventeenth century the scientific academies became unimportant replicas of the literary
academies, consisting of local amateurs and
notables; they were of no importance in
international science.

THE HIGHER EVALUATION OF SCIENCE IN NORTHERN EUROPE

The most obvious aspect of the transformation which occurred in the scientific
movement in Northern Europe was that
there *science eventually became a central
element in an emerging conception of
progress.* This, however, was not at all
clear from the beginning and many aspects
of the movement there appeared to be no
more than a reproduction of Italian patterns. The *rapprochement* between artists
and practical men on the one hand and
scholars of scientific bent on the other,
such as existed in Italy from the fifteenth
century onwards, was copied in Europe in
the sixteenth century. . . . Similarly, the
northern scientific academies owed their
inspiration to Italy. . . .

Nonetheless, as early as the sixteenth
century the differences between the Northern and the Italian patterns became evident
in a variety of forms. The most important
network of scientists and practical men was
that concerned with navigation in England
and Holland.

Contacts between scientists and practical
men were not confined to matters connected with navigation. Apart from the
already mentioned relationships with artists,
engineers and artillery experts, there was
increasing interest in machines, mining,
lens grinding and the making of watches
and other instruments. The field central to
the contacts between scholars and practical
people shifted, in contrast to Italy, from art
and civil and military engineering, which
were primarily the concerns of the ruling
and aristocratic classes, to navigation and
instrument making. These latter fields were
closely tied to the concerns and the fortunes of a new, increasingly numerous and
self-esteeming class of sea traders, merchants and artisans, some of the latter also
dependent primarily on sea trade. . . .

There was an important affinity between
the situation of the merchants and artisans
and that of the new scientific scholars.
Both had more to gain from certain changes
in society than they had to gain from
stability. . . .

THE BIRTH OF A SCIENTISTIC UTOPIA

This vaguely sympathetic stratum was
not, however, sufficient to establish science
in its own right. Man lives not only by
bread but also by the word of God and this
was particularly true in the seventeenth
century. Nearly everyone in Europe was
religious, either Christian or Jewish. . . .

Among the major European religions,
there was however one important difference: Protestantism (a) did not everywhere possess a constituted religious authority, and (b) its doctrines left the interpretation of the Bible to the individual believer
and left him to seek his own religious
enlightenment. Where a Catholic or a Jew
had to suppress what might be his conviction that science would ultimately prove to
be a new way to God because of the fixity
of biblical interpretation, a Protestant who
felt that God's will and the discoveries of
science were in harmony could go ahead
with good conscience, provided that he
lived in an environment where church
authority was unstable or weak. . . .

Thus, while the idea that science and
technology (the "practical arts") could become a better mode of education and an
improved intellectual and moral culture in
general was consistent with the interests
and the outlook of the mobile middle
classes, only certain branches of Protestants

could make scientific knowledge, or a philosophy granting such knowledge complete autonomy, integral to their religious beliefs. Only they could thereby overcome the resistance which religious belief might interpose. Protestantism thus provided the legitimation for the formulation of a new utopian world view where science, experiment and experience — the logical relationship between which was perhaps mistakenly construed — were to form the core of a new culture.

PROTESTANT "SCIENCE POLICY"

In most places Protestants were unable to form a closed religious community. On the one hand, they were in contention with the Catholics; on the other hand, the various Protestant sects fought among themselves. In those situations, no effective religious authority existed to enforce conformity in doctrine and practice. The governments of the territories where these conditions obtained were much freer than any others to adopt a sympathetic attitude to science and the scientistic utopia. Those who believed in the utopia were free to propagate their views and the official authorities could adopt a pragmatic attitude towards the matter. As a result official Protestant authorities adopted on several occasions policies of supporting science and eventually in Commonwealth England they came very near to the scientistic utopia as a basis for their official educational policy. . . .

This was the final stage in the development of the conditions for the emergence of a body of self-conscious and self-confident scientists who looked upon their activities as scientists as something inherently worthy of the efforts of distinguished intellects. Their support now became the official policy of the government of one of the wealthiest and most powerful nations of Europe. Science became, to use Durkheim's phrase, part of *"la vie sérieuse"*; its utilitarian promises were accepted like religious faith and its ethos of dispassionate inquiry, exactitude and empiricism were made into moral values and proudly identified by some with religion. Science had thereby entered definitely into the centre of a newly emerging culture. . . .

SOCIAL CLASS, PROTESTANTISM AND SCIENCE

The emergence of the new type of scientist has thus been linked to the rise of new social classes interested in a more open social structure and a more empirically oriented education on the one hand and to Protestantism on the other. It must be emphasised, however, that the only thing which this explains is the enhancement of the *status* of science and the change in the *role* of the scientist-scholar who now can openly and respectably become a scientist without having to be primarily something else. The change in status helped to increase scientific activity and the change in the definition of the role contributed similarly to the increased systematisation, clarity and boldness of scientific thought. These changes in the status of science and in the distinctiveness of the scientific role do not, however, explain the content of scientific discovery or the composition of the scientific community. Public support and religious grace can heighten motivation but they cannot create talent or determine what it discovers. Public opinion and religious belief cannot even create the basic motivation to engage in science. They can only reinforce or hinder it where it exists in individuals and in the stream of cultural tradition. The content of the new science was overwhelmingly determined by the scholarly tradition which consisted primarily of mathematics, astronomy, dynamics, statics and optics and, secondarily, of the medical fields of anatomy and physiology. Those who cultivated the new sciences had to be educated people with great talent and ample leisure, which meant that they usually came from a wealthy background. The rise of new social classes influenced scientists — whatever their class background might have been — by freeing them from social conventions. They were not inhibited or constrained by considerations of hierarchical dignity from expressing their enthusiasms about experimentation or from thinking in terms of practical utility. . . .

The explanatory factor has, nonetheless, to be sought not in the social and religious characteristics of the scientists of the time but in a constellation which includes the increased numbers, wealth, influence and status of the merchant and artisan classes, Protestantism, the emergence of a scientistic utopia of progress and rising interest in and support for science.

THE CONSOLIDATION OF A EUROPEAN SCIENTIFIC COMMUNITY IN THE SEVENTEENTH CENTURY

With the establishment of the academies possessing sufficient means of support to ensure continuity and to maintain a constant flow of periodical publication, science became more autonomous than it had been hitherto. An uninterrupted scientific activity, more or less proportionate to the general growth of social resources (population and wealth) and relatively independent of the prevailing non-scientific culture, became possible. This contributed greatly to the development of the scientific identity and, beyond it, to the institutionalised role of the modern scientist. . . .

This new situation of science did not make the fortunes of science independent of other social events. But it made science into a social institution with an internal life and structure of its own which could respond autonomously to other social events. The fortunes of science ceased to depend on the fortunes of the social groups and organisations of philosophers and the intellectual developments of philosophy; instead, science became a central focus of an independent group and a new set of institutions. From these, there was a direct path to science as it developed in the nineteenth and twentieth centuries.

SCIENCE AND REFORMATION

REIJER HOOYKAAS

Professor of the History of Science at the Free University, Amsterdam, Reijer Hooykaas (1906—   ) is the author of numerous historical articles on the relationship between science and religion. In his major work, *The Principle of Uniformity in Geology, Biology and Theology* (1963), he systematically explored the philosophical structure of the geological sciences in the nineteenth century and thereby revealed the nature of the metaphysical and scientific elements that met in geology and palaeontology. The article reprinted here is part of a larger projected work on science and Protestantism.

STATISTICAL RESEARCH has established that among the *foreign members* of the Royal Society (in 1829 and in 1869) and the Académie des Sciences (from 1666 to 1883) the Protestants far outnumbered the Roman Catholics. Likewise it has been found that, although in the sixteenth century the Protestants in the southern Netherlands formed but a very small part of the population, their scientific production in quantity and quality surpassed that of Roman Catholic authors, whereas after their expulsion science in Belgium had some difficulties and in the eighteenth century was practically nonexistent. It has also been pointed out that among the group of ten scientists who during the English Commonwealth formed the nucleus that would afterward grow into the Royal Society, seven were decidedly Puritan, whereas on the list of members of the Royal Society of 1663 62 percent (42 of the 68 for whom the religious affiliation is known) *were clearly Puritan,* a percentage still more striking because Puritans constituted a minority of the population.

Efforts have been made to explain this predilection for observational and experimental sciences by the economic ideals of the class to which those Protestants (mainly Calvinists) belonged. Indeed the utilitarian interest in applied science often bore relation to the fact that the investigators belonged to the rising middle class.

The flourishing of exact sciences and technology in Holland about 1600 may be attributed to the expansion of the trade, industry, and navigation of that province, which had no clergy in the proper sense (a reformed minister is not a priest) and almost no nobility. But at the same time there was a great interest in the study of languages (classical and Oriental), botany and zoology, which are not directly "useful." Probably it will always remain impossible to decide whether their economic interests or their religion was first in urging the scientists of England and Holland to research it; in any case the religious share in the rapid growth of science is easily underestimated by those modern historians who cannot imagine that religion was the paramount interest of large groups of the population in the sixteenth and seventeenth centuries and who, consequently, do not take seriously the evidences of religious convictions in the works of the great scientists.

From R. Hooykaas, "Science and Reformation," pp. 258–289. From *The Evolution of Science* by Guy S. Metraux and François Crouzet. Copyright © 1963 by UNESCO. Published by arrangement with The New American Library, Inc., New York. The article originally appeared in *Cahiers d'Histoire Mondiale,* III, no. 1.

For an age in which the religious sanction was necessary to make anything socially acceptable, it made a great difference whether science was condemned, merely tolerated, or positively encouraged by religion.

There is nothing in the dogmas of the three main divisions of Western Christianity — Roman Catholicism, Lutheranism, and Calvinism — to discourage scientific research; great scientists will be found among all three. Yet they do not all three encourage scientific research to the same degree. Max Weber's idea that a special form of the doctrine of election ("Bewährungsglaube," i.e., the belief that performance of "works" is a sign of election) led to a special attitude in economic and, consequently, in scientific endeavor among the Calvinists, has found little favor with experts on Calvinism. Apart from this explanation, however, which indeed seems to oversimplify matters, the work of Weber and especially that of Merton has established the fact that the Reformed (Calvinists, Zwinglians) because of their "innerweltliche Askese" (an intramundane asceticism) were very much inclined toward science. Here a general attitude, an ethical conception of the human task on earth rather than a special dogma seems to have been the main incentive.

In the present paper we will try to expound how the religious attitude of so-called "ascetic" Protestantism, which more or less stood under Calvin's influence, furthered the development of science. . . .

THE GLORY OF GOD

The predilection for scientific research in Protestant circles may be largely explained by the great emphasis laid by Reformed theology upon the central theme: "the glory of God." This has been beautifully worded by Kepler (1571–1630), when he said that being priests of God to the Book of Nature, the astronomers ought to have in their minds not the glory of their own intellect, but above anything else the glory of God (1598).

The Reformed confessions emphasize that God reveals Himself in Scripture and in Nature, "which is before our eyes as a beautiful book, in which all created things, large and small, are like letters, showing the invisible things of God." Recommendation of pious contemplation, however, does not necessarily imply an urge to scientific research. The latter was often regarded as a real danger to religion, not only by medieval asceticism but also by some spiritualistic sects of the sixteenth century (Anabaptists). Reformed theology maintained in opposition to this belief that the duty of glorifying God on account of His works should be performed by all faculties, not only by the eyes but also by the intellect. Calvin deemed those who neglect the study of nature as guilty as those who, when investigating God's works, forget the Creator. He sharply reproved "phantastic" opponents of science as being only fit to make men proud and not as leading to a "knowledge of God and the conduct of ordinary life." Again and again he testified his positive appreciation of scientific research as penetrating deeper into the wonders of nature than mere contemplation. And he does not mean the speculative "physics" of his time, but the real sciences (in the modern sense) of that epoch — astronomy and anatomy, which revealed the secrets of the macrocosm and the microcosm. . . .

THE GENERAL PRIESTHOOD OF BELIEVERS

. . . The Protestant doctrine of the priesthood of all believers proclaimed not only the *right,* but even the *duty* of everybody (who was able to do so) to read the Book of Scripture for himself. As a consequence, likewise the right and duty to read the Book of Nature, without regard to the authority of the fathers of natural philosophy — Aristotle, Pliny, Ptolemy, Galen — was put forward. While fully acknowledging the value of specialized biblical scholarship, the Reformers had nevertheless maintained that the meaning of Scripture is self-evident on essential points and, accordingly, that nobody can be excused by delegating the responsibility for reading Scripture to the hierarchy. In the same way everybody, in principle and according to his capacities, might be a priest to the Book of Creation, in defiance sometimes of the ancient authorities. When Palissy was derided because of his ignorance of the classical languages and hence of the scientific books written therein, he proudly answered that he had obtained his knowledge through the anatomy of nature and not through reading books, for "I have had no book but heaven and earth and it is given to every man to know and read this beautiful book.". . .

The general priesthood of believers is perhaps the only specifically Protestant doctrine that was sometimes consciously, sometimes unconsciously, used to back up science. In any case this doctrine had a large share in framing Protestant thought.

THE BENEFIT OF MANKIND

The glory of God and the benefit of mankind are as closely connected in Christian theology as the two tables of the Law, summarized by Christ as the duty of love for God and our neighbors. Therefore the insistence of Reformed theology on the benefit that may come to mankind from useful inventions in medicine and technique is not a manifestation of the capitalistic mentality of a rising merchant class that hides its mammonistic intentions behind a pious pretense. Here again genuine love for God and one's fellow beings is the main driving force. Even Francis Bacon (1561–1626), often represented as the patron of utilitarianism, was largely inspired by religious motives. He refused to mix up science and theology, but his Calvinistic religion shines out on the pages of his nontheological works. He cited St. Paul in order to proclaim that knowledge without love is vain and that the scientist demonstrates love through the production of works, which are not done for mental satisfaction alone. "La science pour la science" is totally opposed to Reformed ethics; the glory of God and the invention of useful

things to lessen the burdens of human life are the final aims of science. . . .

EMPIRICISM

The Reformers wanted to keep exclusively to the record of divine revelation as written down in the Bible. They wished to abolish what they considered rationalistic, superfluous additions to the biblical revelation and to return to the pure source. A parallel attitude was assumed toward the Book of Creation. In the interpretation of nature the same sense of responsibility prevailed as in the exegesis of Scripture: they were anxious not to deviate from the true meaning of the Bible, so they felt religiously bound to nature. Here also they considered themselves to be on holy ground, confronted with a book of God that had to be accepted even when not completely understood. . . .

This empiricism led the experimental scientists to a mild skepticism, even toward their own theories. The geographical discoveries had exploded all philosophical reasoning about the division of land and water and about the inhabited parts of the earth. Here bare facts overthrew all clever theories. The unexpected discovery of countries with human inhabitants, animals, and plants never dreamed of proved the possibility of the seemingly marvelous and corroborated the religious acknowledgment of God's infinite power. As William Watts remarked: the *thoughts* of the philosophers were contradicted by the *unexpected observations* of the navigators. As age-old prejudices crumbled down, a remarkable freedom of thought and openness toward new inventions and discoveries was created. The seventeenth-century scientists liked to say that there are no "columns of Hercules," no *ne plus ultra* in philosophy. This led them, especially the followers of Bacon (who very often were Puritans or, like Bacon himself, were influenced by Puritanism), to propound audacious hypotheses. Precisely the fact that hypotheses were regarded as only provisory, and that, consequently, a suspension of judgment was indispensable until experience had confirmed a supposition, caused this freedom of theorizing. . . .

"ENTHUSIASM" AND SCIENCE

When Calvin wrote against those "phantastic people" who decry all sciences because they would only make man arrogant and lead him away from God, he was thinking of spiritualists like the Anabaptists. In the upheaval of the English Civil War such spiritualistic sects came to the fore and in 1653 Parliament even considered the suppression of universities as heathenish and unnecessary. However, the majority "gave a stop to their frenzy." In 1657 Cromwell had to protect Oxford against Anabaptist hostility. The members of the spiritualistic sects like the Quakers in England, the Labadists and the Mennonites in Holland, were not very friendly toward human learning in general. Their aversion to school theology was of the same nature as that of some otherwise very culturally inclined Puritans (like Webster); their dislike of metaphysical philosophy they shared with all opponents of rationalism, their indifference to science took its origin in a type of asceticism that approached monastic "ausserweltliche Askese." But the Mennonites had, before 1620, already ceased their opposition to learning, whereas the Quakers soon took an active interest in applied science.

On the other hand, many conservative clergymen, supported by political reactionaries, were more afraid of science than most sectarians. They regarded it as a danger to the established church, and after the Restoration of the Stuarts, Joseph Glanvill, Robert Boyle, and Thomas Sprat did much to refute their arguments, especially as the charge of puritanism ("enthusiasm" or "fanaticism") as well as that of deism and atheism was made against the "virtuosi." Now it has already been made evident that those who were most radical in their return to "Scripture alone" in theology (to wit, the Reformed, Zwinglians, and Calvinists, or, in general, the puritanically minded) were also most radical in their support of a direct inquiry into nature by experiment and observation, which was the ideal of the Royal Society, which was founded shortly after the Restoration. . . .

AUTHORITY IN SCIENCE

Experience versus reason was the background of empiricism. This includes also experience versus the reason of the ancients, experience versus authority. The opposition to human authority appealed very strongly to the Reformed. Their mind had been trained to the idea that one has to find out the truth for oneself and that there ought to be independence of human authority in order that the submission to divine authority be the more complete. The general laicization must have influenced also their scientific attitude. New ideas could easily get hold of them, and were at least not rejected because of their nonconformity to traditional beliefs. No ecclesiastical censure on books and scientific ideas was officially applied by a central body of discipline, and scholastic philosophy was not officially connected with theology. When for example the great Dutch theologian Gisbertus Voetius (1588–1676) defended the Aristotelian philosophy as a necessary support of orthodox Protestant theology, his opponents of the Cocceian party either divorced philosophy from theology, or inclined to Cartesianism. When Voetius regarded the geocentric world picture as the only one compatible with Scripture, the no less orthodox Cocceians freely adhered to Copernicanism without interference of synods or church consistories.

In spite of their reverence for the Fathers of the Church, the Reformers never forsook a critical and free attitude toward them. Likewise the Protestant scientists liked to point out against their Romish opponents who recognized "Tradition" as well as Scripture as a source of revelation, how many mistakes the Church Fathers and the popes had made in scientific matters. The Reformation might signify to some of its adherents a return to the church of the first centuries, but to the majority it was a return to Scripture. In the same way many naturalists were not content with rejecting medieval commentators but also wished to be free from classical antiquity, as they wanted to return to Nature herself. Of course this led to exaggeration, but on the whole this iconoclasm was healthy for the development of science. It was necessary that criticism of the ancients and consciousness of the value of the present age should replace the adoration of the past. . . .

MANUAL LABOR

The love for experimental science and the technological interest of the Reformed were closely interwoven with their ethical evaluation of manual labor. Experimentation often derives the choice as well as the solution of its problems from the crafts, and now that the speculative occupations were to a certain extent devaluated, there was, even amongst the learned, less disrespect for manual labor. In principle manual labor had never been slighted by Jewish and Christian ethics as it had been in late antiquity and, perhaps under the influence thereof, by the humanists. . . .

The Reformed matrimonial service of the Netherlands calls upon the husband to "labor faithfully and diligently in his Divine calling," and this was certainly more than a pious phrase. Isaac Beeckman, although a theologian and a medical doctor, did not deem it below his dignity to be a chandler and manufacturer of water conduits. He found therein abundant occasions for experiments in mechanics, hydrostatics, and hydrodynamics, and he abandoned this profession only when the headmastership of a Latin school seemed to offer more leisure for pursuing scientific investigations. Esteem for manual labor and diligence in "industries" were regarded as the main causes for the increased wealth of the Hollanders and the improvement of their minds; they "not only disgraced, but terrified their neighbors by their industry.". . .

The experimental and empirical character of the new science made the cooperation of the craftsmen indispensable. More than the philosophers they were confronted with hard facts. Confidence in wrong theories on ebb and flood tide or on the magnetic needle could cause a disastrous end of a sailor's life. Therefore, the advocates of "new philosophy" mocked their opponents for shunning manual operations and extolled the simple artisan as being nearer the truth. And did not the craftsmen have every reason for their growing self-esteem? Had not the first effective blow to traditional science been delivered by the seafarers who crossed the Torrid Zone, discovered the inhabitants of the Southern Hemisphere (against the opinion of Greek philosophers as well as that of Christian Church Fathers), and found a new world with plants and animals unheard of in the books of Greek and medieval naturalists? Not a new theory but simple *facts,* discovered by simple people, overthrew the old philosophy. The same was true of experimentation: "Simple workmen were capable of convicting of error all great men who are called philosophers" (Pascal). . . .

THE SOURCE OF NATURAL SCIENCE

To the modern reader it seems self-evident that the science of nature should be founded upon the observation of nature, the stellar universe, the earth, the plants, and animals. Yet other possibilities presented themselves in the sixteenth century, namely (1) the writings of the ancients, (2) immediate enlightenment, (3) rational reflection, and (4) Holy Scripture. Therefore, further consideration is needed to explain why the Reformed in general had chosen the Book of Creation as the fifth possibility.

1. The Reformed were sometimes enticed by the writings of the ancients. Bookish people were attracted by the parallel between the return to the oldest documents of Christian religion and the oldest documents of human science. In general, however, this humanistic attitude did not prevail.

2. As to the second possibility, just as

some people founded their religion largely upon divine illumination by the Spirit (Anabaptists, Quakers), there were theosophists who expected scientific enlightenment from an immediate insight into the hidden workings of nature. Renaissance mysticism (neopythagoreanism, hermetism, alchemy) furthered the idea that man (microcosm) by a sympathetic feeling could immediately grasp the inner essence of the universe (macrocosm). Kepler's rejection of the scientific esotericism of the Rosicrucian Robert Fludd was paralleled by the attitude of the Reformers toward the "enthusiasts" and theosophists.

3. The third way to science, that of logical deduction from innate ideas, had little attraction for people who attributed small value to "natural theology" because of their distrust of "unaided" reason. Bacon's violent opposition to logic-spinning in science was a reflection of the Puritan attitude and, consequently, was much appreciated by the Puritans. . . .

4. The fourth possibility presented the greatest temptation to the Reformed. Because of their principle of founding theology and ethics (and often politics also) upon Scripture, it was easy to draw the parallel of founding science too upon Scriptural data. Scientific research, then, only served to elaborate and to detail a discipline of which the principles were already known by the exegesis of the Bible. . . .

It could be expected that those Protestants with whom biblicism was the strongest, i.e., the Puritans, would be the staunchest opponents of the motion of the earth. Yet, the reverse is true. In England Th. Digges (1573), John Bainbridge (1618), Henry Gellibrand (1634), John Wallis, and John Wilkins (1640) were Puritan supporters of the Copernican system, and this open-mindedness to new and bold ideas went even further. In 1576 Digges put forward the theory that the fixed stars are at varying distances beyond the orb of Saturn, thereby breaking through the closed, spherical universe that Copernicus had not abandoned and that Kepler and Galileo would

adhere to. Not the Italian freethinker Giordano Bruno, but Thomas Digges was the first to propound this audacious hypothesis. Wilkins also accepted the idea of an infinite universe; he ascribed the opposition of Copernicus to servility to the ancients and to the fear of deviation from the exegesis of Scripture phrases as given by "the supposed infallible Church."

CALVINISM AND COPERNICANISM

The main reason for the open attitude of so many Reformed authors toward the movement of the earth seems to be that their biblicism was related only to religious (historical, ethical, ecclesiastical) aspects, not to scientific topics. As a rule they gave little room to "Mosaic" science and sought indeed the data of science in the Book of Creation. One of the reasons for this must have been the example set by Calvin, their greatest theological teacher. First of all, it is important that Calvin, notwithstanding his severe critique on Greek philosophers, did not reject everything that originated with the heathen, but carefully tested each of their ideas on its own merits. In principle, the same was done by those conservative theologians (Roman Catholic as well as Protestant) who put the Aristotelian world system to the test of Scripture and were of the opinion that there was perfect agreement. Calvin, however, saw more clearly than any of his contemporaries that the world picture of the Bible conflicted with the Aristotelian system. . . .

Consequently, it is to Calvin's great credit that he recognized the discrepancy between the scientific world system of his days and the biblical text, and secondly that he did not repudiate the results of scientific research on that account. It is quite irrelevant that Calvin did not know the Copernican system. If the Aristotelian system is not in the Bible and yet may be true, the Scriptural argument for the rejection of every other astronomical system is without value; from the religious point of view the old system henceforth loses its advantages over the Copernican system. . . .

There is a tendency to contrast the presumably milder and more cultural attitude of High Church Anglicanism and Roman Catholicism to a conventional caricature of Puritanism and Calvinism as a cold, unemotional, static orthodoxy. "Calvinism has usually been discussed in an atmosphere of controversy and has often been judged, even by academicians, with slender reference to the evidence."

The myth of the Puritan hatred of music and art has been exploded by P. A. Scholes; that Calvin and Puritanism had a stimulating influence upon science has been made evident by several recent studies. "Puritanism was an important factor . . . in promoting the type of thinking that helped to arouse interest in science" (Stimson). "Calvinism or puritanism or ascetic protestantism generally . . . played no small part in arousing a sustained interest in science." "The happy marriage of these two movements was based on an intrinsic compatibility" (Merton). The religion of the Reformed neither regarded grace as an addition to nature, nor as an antithesis to it, but closely intertwined them. Consequently, a radical renewal of every department of life — church and state, individual and society, morals and science — was their aim. It seems evident that they achieved considerable success with respect to science.

CATHOLICISM, PROTESTANTISM, AND SCIENCE

FRANÇOIS RUSSO

The French Jesuit François Russo (1909–   ) has undertaken the difficult task of replying to those who see a natural affinity between science and Protestantism. Unlike his Protestant counterparts, Russo cannot turn to a relatively large body of secondary literature to support his claims. However, as the author of a history of scientific thought and the compiler of a widely used bibliography covering research in the history of science—*Histoire des Sciences et des Techniques: Bibliographie* (Paris, 1964, 2nd ed.)—he is well equipped to gather evidence for the Catholic interpretation.

There is a definite need for concentrated historical and sociological studies into the relationship between Catholicism and early modern science. These studies would dispel the popular, and prejudiced, claim that in all times, and all places, the Catholic Church and dogma have been hostile to scientific activity.

THE RESPECTIVE CONTRIBUTIONS OF CATHOLICS AND PROTESTANTS TO THE PROGRESS OF SCIENCE

... [T]HE GENERAL STATISTICS for scientists, drawn up by Candolle[1] and drawn upon by J. Pelseneer, should be used with great caution; in any case they do not begin until 1666, when the Paris Académie des Sciences was founded, and are consequently of little help for the period with which we are dealing. They do, however, confirm one important point—that the Spanish contribution to scientific progress was extremely slight. Spanish historians themselves admit the fact. Spain's only contributions of any importance—and even those are not fundamental—were made in the sphere of the natural sciences; and to lend weight even to this statement we are compelled to couple the name of one genuine Catholic Spaniard, Francisco Vallès (1520–1592), who did remarkable work in epidemiology, with those of a Jewish doctor, Antonio Gomez Pereira, who lived in the first half of the sixteenth century, and a "heretic," Michel Servet (1509–1553), a nonconformist Protestant who was burned at Geneva òn Calvin's orders.

Though the fact of Spain's deficiencies is undeniable, some caution should be observed in suggesting explanations for this state of affairs. I will not pause to refute Candolle's oversimple view that it was due chiefly to the Inquisition. Nobody can seriously maintain that the Spanish Inquisition was censorious to a degree that made it impossible for Spaniards even to study geometry, optics, or botany. The cause of the weakness appears to be mainly cultural. The Spanish are above all a spiritual, artistic, and literary people. Should we hold this against them? Surely there should be some variety in the cultural attitudes of different nations—regrettable though it

[1] Alphonse de Candolle, *Histoire des Sciences et des Savants depuis Deux Siècles* (Geneva, 1873). Jean Pelseneer's studies are listed in the "Suggestions for Additional Reading." [Ed. note.]

From François Russo, "Catholicism, Protestantism, and the Development of Science in the Sixteenth and Seventeenth Centuries," pp. 309–319; trans. by Daphne Woodward. From *The Evolution of Science* by Guy S. Metraux and François Crouzet. Copyright © 1963 by UNESCO. Published by arrangement with The New American Library, Inc., New York. The article originally appeared in *Cahiers d'Histoire Mondiale*, Vol. III, no. 4.

may be that this indifference to science should have been carried so far.

As for the other countries, there is no need of statistics to show that, broadly speaking, it is incorrect to claim that the Protestant countries far outdistanced the Catholic ones in the field of scientific activity. Taking the population figures into account, it may be admitted that the balance is slightly in favor of the Protestants. But are statistics of this kind valid in cultural matters? In any case, to mention a general impression to which I will return later when discussing individual fields of study, it may safely be said that the countries with a majority of Catholics, such as France, and those that were entirely Catholic, such as Italy, contributed at least as much to the progress of science as did the Protestant countries, foremost of which were England and the Netherlands. It should be remembered that scientific activity in Italy was exceptionally brilliant, at least up to 1650. Omitting the well-known names to which I shall return later on, we may recall the universities of Padua and Bologna, the famous Accademia dei Lincei in Rome — which was forced to close in 1651 — and, in the latter half of the seventeenth century, the Accademia del Cimento, at Florence. The vitality of science in France, where it was pursued almost solely by Catholics, is too well known to require stressing. It is, however, true that after the middle of the seventeenth century the scientific movement in France and Italy showed some decline in vigor, though this was not as marked as Protestant historians have asserted, and that on the other hand there was a considerable increase of scientific activity in England and the Netherlands. But the analysis given in previous sections points to the conclusion that this was due not to religious but to cultural and economic causes. This statement, of course, needs to be confirmed by further elaboration, for which this brief study allows no space. We should look into the possibility that scientific progress may have been impeded by the fact that in the Catholic countries the university education of clergy and monks was under the more or less direct control of the ecclesiastical authorities — as, for instance, in France at the Sorbonne — and made very little allowance for the progress of scientific thought. One suspects that this was the case, but in the present state of knowledge it is impossible to be absolutely positive. Similar inquiry should be made into the censorship of books before publication. It seems likely that interesting unpublished documents on this subject might be forthcoming.

Let us now turn to what is in my opinion the most important aspect of the matter — one that I am surprised to see was somewhat neglected by R. Hooykaas and J. Pelseneer — the investigation *subject by subject* of the part played by Protestants and Catholics, respectively, in the progress of science.

I shall not attempt to cover the whole range of subjects, but only the most important among them, with special reference to those in which particularly striking advances were made during the period with which we are concerned. This means reviewing, in succession, mathematics, astronomy, mechanics, optics, electricity, the sciences dealing with the soil and with biology (botany, zoology, human anatomy, physiology), and finally the applied physical sciences. I shall refer only to the most distinguished scientists in each branch. But as I said in my introductory remarks on methodology, I shall also give some brief particulars of the contribution made to progress in these subjects by the clergy and more especially by the Company of Jesus, whose scientific activity covered a field the extent of which historians have hitherto, perhaps, not fully realized. The fact that, except for the contributions of a few outstanding figures, the results of this activity were not really fundamental should not surprise us, science being, in the ordinary way, not the principal occupation of clerics. But, as already mentioned, it was of great importance to the spread of science and its introduction into education. Protestant education, at least in France, was less open-minded.

Mathematics. The great mathematical advances of the sixteenth and seventeenth centuries were due principally to work in three nations — Italy, France, and England. Unless I am mistaken, the most notable French mathematicians were all Catholics with the exception of Viète, the founder of modern algebra, who was a Protestant. The English mathematicians were, on the contrary, all Protestants.

The most important contributions made to algebra in the sixteenth century — apart from those of Viète, who was in a class of his own — came from the Italians Cardan (1501–1576), Tartaglia (1505–1557), and Bombelli (1530 — ?). In the seventeenth century advances in algebra were due chiefly to Descartes, to the Englishman Harriot (1560–1621), and to the Frenchman Albert Girard (1595–1632). To Descartes we owe, in particular, the invention of analytical geometry.

Differential and integral calculus owed its first development to the Italian Cavalieri (1598–1647), who was a member of the Order of Jesuati (not Jesuiti), the Frenchman Roberval (1602–1675), the Belgian Jesuit Grégoire de Saint Vincent (1584–1647), Blaise Pascal (1623–1662), Pierre Fermat (1601–1665) — who also made some very penetrating research into the theory of numbers — the Dutch Protestant Huygens (1629–1695), the Englishmen Wallis (1616–1703), James Gregory (1638–1675), and above all, of course, Newton (1642–1727), the German Protestant Leibniz (1646–1716), and the Protestant Jacques Bernoulli, of Basle (1654–1705).

In geometry France takes the lead, with Descartes, Pascal, Desargues (1591–1662), and La Hire (1640–1718).

An invention that came as a sidelight, but that was of great practical importance, was that of logarithms, by the Englishman Napier (or Neper) (1550–1617).

Although, apart from Grégoire de Saint Vincent, the Jesuits had no mathematicians of the first rank, they produced some estimable books and used them in connection with teaching which, though admittedly elementary, they imparted in an intelligent and stimulating manner. The commentary on Euclid by Calvius, which contains a wealth of shrewd observations, had a wide circulation in the learned world as well as in the Jesuit colleges. Mention should also be made of the works on quadratures by Fathers de la Faille (1597–1652) and Guldin (1577–1643), of that by Father Fabri (1606–1685) on the squaring of the cycloid — an important contribution to the progress of infinitesimal calculus — and of the work on the calculation of centers of gravity, by Father Lalouvère (1600–1664). *Récréations mathématiques* (1624), by Father Leurechon (1591–1670), is also not without scientific interest and enjoyed great popularity.

This short review shows us that Catholics and Protestants alike made contributions to the construction of the science of mathematics in the sixteenth and seventeenth centuries, and that it is hard to say which group played the greater part.

Astronomy and mechanics. The same applies to the admirable discoveries, from Copernicus to Newton, from which modern astronomy and mechanics emerged. After a "revolution" had been effected by Nicolas Copernicus, Canon of Cracow (1473–1543), astronomy made tremendous progress thanks to the Protestant Kepler (1571–1630), whose efforts in the field of science were manifestly supported by mystical inspiration; but it was not he who, strictly speaking, established the celestial mechanism. This achievement resulted from the efforts of the Catholics Descartes and Galileo (1564–1642) and the Protestants Huygens (1629–1695), Hooke (1635–1703), and finally Newton. A considerable, though minor, contribution was also made by two Catholics, the Italian Borelli (1608–1679) and the Frenchman Bouillant (1605–1694), who had been converted from Calvinism at the age of twenty-two.

In addition to this major work, the progress of astronomy is denoted by the increasing number of observations, which became much more precise and accurate as instruments were improved and new ones invented. Chief among these was the telescope; the story of its invention is still obscure, but it seems to have been due to the joint efforts of Dutchmen and Italians, and was used for the first time in 1610, by Galileo.

The Jesuits took a great interest in astronomy. They had numerous observatories, the best known of which were at Prague, Rome, and Ingolstadt. But they also made interesting observations in the others, chiefly those in France, such as the observatory attached to their college at Avignon. Father Clavius was chiefly responsible for the reform of the calendar in 1582. Father Scheiner (1575–1650) discovered sunspots in 1610, at the same time as Galileo. Father Zucci (1586–1670) had the first idea of the reflector telescope. In their foreign missions the Jesuits undertook important astronomic work. Especially in China, where they introduced European astronomy and reformed the calendar; leading figures in these considerable undertakings were Fathers Terrentius (1576–1630), a founder member of the Accademia dei Lincei, Schall (1592–1665), and Verbiest (1623–1688). The last of these equipped the imperial observatory at Peking with magnificent instruments, constructed under his supervision and still to be seen there. The Jesuit missionaries were also required to communicate the results of their observations to the European academies, and some of them aroused great interest, especially those dealing with the calculation of longitude.

The Jesuits also distinguished themselves as map-makers; an Italian, Ricci (1552–1610), was the first to correct the gross errors in the depiction of China in sixteenth-century atlases; another Italian, Martini (1614–1661), drew up a map of China in which he reveals a great mastery of technique; it was published at Amsterdam in 1655 with the title *Atlas sinensis* and earned considerable praise.

Optics. Though the greatest advances in optics during the seventeenth century were made by Newton, the work of his predecessors was by no means negligible. Here again it is impossible to say which creed had the advantage of the other. Side by side with the Protestants Snellius (1591–1626), Kepler, Huygens, and Römer (1644–1710) are the names of Catholics such as Descartes, the Jesuit Grimaldi (1631–1663), who was the first to formulate the theory of wave mechanics, the Abbé Mariotte (1620–1684), Malebranche (1638–1715), and Fermat (1601–1665).

Magnetism and electricity. Here again a Protestant name dominates — that of the Englishman Gilbert (1544–1603); but Father Cabeo, a Jesuit (1602–1650), also deserves mention for the important new views set forth in his *Philosophia magnetica*. In addition to the experiments conducted by the Dutch Protestant Otto von Guericke (1602–1686) there were those carried out at Florence by the Accademia del Cimento and continued later by the Royal Society. Here again it seems impossible to give the palm to one creed rather than the other.

Geology, paleontology, mineralogy. Here the great pioneer is a Protestant, Bernard Palissy (1510–1589). At war with dogmatism and facile, conventional views, Palissy put forward ideas about the construction of the earth and the nature of fossils whose originality and accuracy were to remain unappreciated for a long time. More than a century later, the chief progress in the geological sciences was made by a Danish Catholic, Nils Stensen (or Steno) (1638–1686), a convert from Protestantism, who became a priest and ended his life as an archbishop. His *De solido intra solidum naturaliter contento* (Florence, 1669) lays the foundations of stratigraphy and crystallography. This latter discipine also owed noteworthy progress to the Englishman, Hooke, with his celebrated *Micrographia* (1665).

Other, though minor, contributors to this aspect of science were the English Protestant Martin Lister (1638–1712) and Father

Kircher, whom I have already mentioned. In his huge *Mundus subterraneus* (1665, 2 vols., folio) Kircher includes much information that is unscientific and often mythical; but he makes a number of pertinent remarks and above all he had an enthusiastic desire to find out about the nature of the terrestrial globe that was calculated to turn men's minds toward a branch of research to which serious scientists had until then paid scant attention.

Natural sciences. Here again there is no marked superiority of one confession over the other. R. Hooykaas is of course correct in pointing out the importance of the role of Protestants in sixteenth-century botany. There was the German school, with its strong Lutheran affiliations, which included Brunfels (1470–1534), Jerome Bock (1498–1551), and Leonhardt Fuchs (1501–1566); at Basle there was Gaspard Bauhin (1560–1624); l'Escluse (1526–1609), a native of Antwerp who lived in France for a time and spent his last years in England, was probably the most eminent of the Protestant botanists; and at Montpellier there was the Frenchman, l'Obel (1538–1616).

But Catholic Italy produced Mattioli (1500–1577), a very keen observer, Andrea Cesalpino (1519–1603), the greatest of the sixteenth-century botanists, the first to suggest a lucid classification of plants — in his celebrated *De Plantis* (1583), and Aldrovandi (1522–1605), who founded the first botanical garden, at Bologna.

During the seventeenth century there are two outstanding names in botany — the English Protestant John Ray (1627–1705) and the French Catholic Tournefort (1656–1708), who made the greatest contribution to the establishment of a system that was put forward by any botanist before Linnaeus.

The leading sixteenth-century zoologists were the Protestant Gesner (1516–1565) of Basle, and Rondelet (1507–1566), a doctor of Montpellier, declared by R. Hooykaas, following the authority of Arber, to be one of the leaders of the Reformation in southern France, whereas the Protestant historians themselves admit that it is difficult to prove that he ever passed from Catholicism to Protestantism. Rondelet's book on fish, *De piscibus* (1554), is remarkable for the period, and even Linnaeus referred to it. Mention should also be made of the French Catholic Belon (1517–1564), who is universally recognized as the founder of comparative anatomy.

In human anatomy one name towers above the rest — that of the Belgian Catholic Vésale (1514–1564). Vesalius taught for many years at Padua and also lived for some time in Spain. He wrote the famous *De humani corporis fabrica* (1543). Others who distinguished themselves at Padua were the Italians Fallope (1523–1562) and, still more, his nephew, Fabrizio d'Acquapendente (1537–1619).

The greatest name in surgery is that of the French Protestant Ambroise Paré (1510–1590).

His discovery of the circulation of the blood is the great claim to glory of the English Protestant Harvey (1578–1657). But back in the sixteenth century a pupil of Vesalius, Realdo Colombo (1516–1559), and the Protestant Michel Servet (1511–1553) had discovered the circulation of the blood in the lungs, and Cesalpino the valvules of the veins.

Fabrizio d'Acquapendente may be regarded as the founder of embryology. Research on this subject was considerably stimulated in the seventeenth century by the Italian Redi (1626–1697).

The movement of animals and the functioning of the muscles were the subject of an important book by the Italian Borelli (1608–1679), who, as we have seen, also gained distinction in mechanics and astronomy.

Microscopic biology originated in the seventeenth century, receiving its most important contributions from the Italian Malpighi (1628–1694), who was the first to demonstrate the circulation of the blood in the capillaries, and the Dutch Protestants Swammerdam (1637–1682) and Van Leeuwenhoek (1632–1723). Thanks to the microscope, the latter discovered unicellular living organisms.

Applied physical sciences. I will confine myself, in this immense field, to providing a few particulars to controvert the widespread impression that Protestantism was chiefly responsible for guiding science into practical channels. There is, in my opinion, little justification for this view. Protestant England did, indeed, play an important part in the development of mechanical technology from the seventeenth century onward; but France and Italy also have remarkable achievements to their credit in this respect, as was recently pointed out by Bertrand Gille in his general study entitled *Les problèmes techniques au XVIIe siècle.*

It is also worthwhile to mention the contribution made by clerics, and particularly Jesuits, to applied science. The Jesuits gave a distinctly practical slant to the teaching of science in their own colleges, and also held chairs in numerous French universities where they taught hydrography, training students in marine subjects. They were interested in shipbuilding as well; Father Hoste (1652–1700), for instance, published a *Théorie de la construction des vaisseaux* (Lyon, 1697), which was respected by the technicians. Other Jesuits, such as Father Milliet de Chales, interested themselves in the art of fortification. The construction of machines was the favorite subject of the celebrated Father Schott (1608–1666), and his *Technica curiosa* (Nuremberg, 1664) had a wide circulation. Father Lana-Terzi (1631–1687), an Italian, was one of the chief pioneers of flight.

CONCLUSION

The foregoing account, and the methodological observations that accompany it, has, I hope, shown the great difficulty of determining the influence of religious attitude, whether Protestant or Catholic, on the development of science in the sixteenth and seventeenth centuries, and what share of any such influence was possessed by either creed. To conclude — as J. Pelseneer does after analyzing in a few pages the statistics of scientists in each confession — that "modern science was born of the Reformation" seems to me to make a really excessive departure from the most elementary requirements of the historical method. The slightly longer consideration given to the subject in this article indicates far less categorical and obvious conclusions, which may be summed up as follows:

1. The Protestant attitude in religion provided, in the majority of cases, but not always, an atmosphere that doubtless fostered scientific progress inasmuch as it encouraged the study of nature and left scientists to work without restriction.

2. Taken as a whole, Catholicism was at least equally receptive toward those branches of science that emanated from its own doctrine and spiritual outlook. The work of the Company of Jesus, in particular, was marked by a Humanism very favorable to science and not met with to the same extent in Protestantism.

As for freedom of scientific research, though it may sometimes have been unduly restricted owing to religious considerations — the case of Galileo is a notable example of this — there is no evidence that such interference seriously impeded the progress of science. In any case, Protestantism offers similar examples of such methods, which may be imputed, on both sides, to a conventional outlook and a failure to distinguish clearly between the scientific and religious fields.

3. While it is true that the Protestant countries displayed remarkable scientific activity, that of the Catholic countries, or at least of France and Italy, seems to have been equally intense, except perhaps in the case of Italy toward the end of the seventeenth century.

4. There is no really conclusive evidence that scientific activity, whether in Catholic

or Protestant countries, was connected with religious attitude. In any case there are cultural and economic factors of at least equal importance to be taken into account.

5. While comprehensive statistics for scientists of the two creeds are difficult to obtain for the period under consideration, and are not very illuminating, it is interesting to investigate the respective parts played by Catholics and Protestants in the advance of the different branches of science. This leads to the conclusion that, numerically speaking, Protestants and Catholics seem to have shared equally in these developments.

6. The preceding conclusion does not necessarily imply that Protestantism and Catholicism influenced scientific development to precisely the same extent, for:

a. Numerical conclusions give only a rough idea of an infinitely complex situation — viz. the making of discoveries and their exploitation.

b. It still remains to be determined, for each individual scientist, what was the connection between his religious attitude and the scientific research on which he was engaged. In most cases the connection seems to have been somewhat tenuous.

7. The foregoing conclusion leads us to recognize that, especially from the seventeenth century onward, scientific development became more and more a question of technical method and thus grew fairly independent of religious attitudes. This is another aspect of the process of secularization, the effect of which was to remove scientific demonstration from the sphere of religion — a process that arose, not from rejection of religious beliefs, but from a more correct understanding of their nature.

In conclusion I should like to express my gratitude to R. Hooykaas. Though I have differed from him on some points, his stimulating views have nevertheless been most helpful. I am glad, too, that by concentrating chiefly on the role of Catholicism in the development of science during the century of the Reformation, my article provides a supplement to his. The two thus combine to form a basis for future amplifications and discussion in an atmosphere of open-mindedness and deep mutual esteem.

THE PSYCHOLOGICAL REVOLUTION:
The Emotional Source of the Scientific Movement

LEWIS S. FEUER

A list of the books produced by Lewis S. Feuer (1912–   ) is a good measure of the breadth of his interests: *Psychoanalysis and Ethics* (1955), *Spinoza and the Rise of Liberalism* (1958), ed. *Marx and Engels: Basic Writings on Politics and Philosophy* (1959). From these works he turned to his psychological explanation of the emergence of modern science and his criticism of the Weber-Merton thesis. Because Feuer's major research interests were outside of the mainstream of the history of science he was better able to challenge the assumptions of those who accepted the Protestant interpretation. At the same time, however, this isolation deprived him of some of the fundamental insights and values gained by those scholars who had been concentrating upon the internal, conceptual growth of science.

Feuer has taught philosophy and the social sciences at the University of Vermont and at the Berkeley campus of the University of California. He is now a member of the faculty of the University of Toronto.

T HE RISE OF SCIENCE is the great distinctive intellectual phenomenon of modern times. The scientific movement that emerged in the seventeenth century brought a promise of progress and of the realization of man's deepest hopes. It proposed not only to liberate men from ignorance but also to free them from superstition, religious hatred, irksome toil, and war. For science was then not the pursuit of technicians; it was the "new philosophy," as Francis Bacon called it, the "active science," the first genuine alternative that had been contrived to dogma, myth, and taboo. The world of medieval gloom that denigrated the powers of man gave way to an optimistic faith in his capacities. The scientist of the seventeenth century was a philosophical optimist; delight and joy in man's status pervaded his theory of knowledge and of the universe. And it was this revolution in man's emotions which was the basis for the change in his ideas.

Behind the history of ideas lies the history of emotions. Every major intellectual movement is preceded by the advent of new kinds of feelings that shape the new mode in which reality is to be intellectually apprehended. Emotions determine the perspective, the framework, for the explanation of the perceived world. Whatever the social and economic forces that are operative in the background of people's lives, they impinge on men's ideas through the intervening channel of feeling and emotion. The categories and forms of explanation that characterize the thinking of any given era are thus intimately connected with its underlying emotional structure.

That the birth of modern science was linked to the rise in Western Europe of a new sensibility — what I would call an ethics of freedom — was candidly avowed by philosophers, historians, and scientists in the eighteenth and nineteenth centuries. The Victorian era, in which men such as W. E. H. Lecky and Thomas Henry Huxley lived, saw the promise of the seven-

From *The Scientific Intellectual* by Lewis S. Feuer, © 1963 by Basic Books, Inc., Publishers, New York, pp. 1–19.

teenth century being fulfilled in its own time — in such great generalizations as the law of conservation of energy and the theory of natural selection, and in the discoveries in electrodynamics which opened prospects for human use even more imposing than the mechanical forces that the seventeenth century had released. The telegraph, the wireless, the dynamo were regarded as only beginnings, and it was serenely assumed that they would be followed by a series of inventions and scientific advances which would be the instruments of man's progress.

The youthful optimism of the seventeenth century and the mature confidence of the nineteenth have, however, in the twentieth century given place to philosophies of torment and despair. As science in practical purport becomes more destructive, the scientist and philosopher speak all the more of the theoretical "impotence principles" of modern physics. Einstein, with his belief in the possibility of a determinate complete system of physical theory, has come to be regarded as essentially a classical, Victorian personality. As the scientist's work, moreover, has become more of a job in an institutionalized and bureaucratized setting, he has surrendered the optimistic self-dedication which characterized his predecessors. The contemporary scientist usually advocates no "new" philosophy; instead he shares the prevalent ideology and values.

The twentieth century has likewise produced a new sociology of science, which aims to discard the union of liberal values with science. The optimistic standpoint of the nineteenth-century spokesman of science is generally regarded today as naïve. The contemporary sociology of science stresses especially the irrational sources of scientific inquiry; it tends to regard the rise of science as a by-product of man's neurotic striving. When the erudite German sociologist, Max Weber, affirmed half a century ago that "the empiricism of the seventeenth century was the means for asceticism to seek God in nature," he was in

effect challenging the whole notion, affirmed throughout the previous three centuries, that the spirit of scientific research was born of hedonist-libertarian values. Empirical science, as the outcome of ascetic repression, was conceived instead as rooted in human self-aggression. . . .

Weber's impressive sociological theory was largely conceived as a reply and alternative to the historical materialism of Karl Marx. Weber denied that material and technical interests were the motive forces in the origin of science; the primary causal factor was Protestant asceticism, combined with the belief that "the knowledge of God and His designs can only be attained through a knowledge of His works. . . ." The scientific investigation of Nature is held to have been the way that ascetic Protestants sought to find God. This standpoint has found especial support in the influential writings of the American sociologist Robert K. Merton, and has become a familiar proposition in contemporary social science. Merton enunciated what has been the dominant view for a generation: When the evidence is examined, he wrote, "Puritanism, and ascetic Protestantism generally, emerge as an emotionally consistent system of beliefs, sentiments, and action which played no small part in arousing a sustained interest in science." Contemporary psychoanalytical theory seemed likewise to support the notion that Protestant asceticism was the mainspring of modern science. According to Freud, man's achievements in the arts and sciences are the product of a repression and sublimation of energies; scientific curiosity is sexual curiosity altered by a repressive agent. It was thus consistent with psychoanalytical theory to maintain that Protestant sexual repression had caused a redirection of human energies into scientific research. According to both Weber and Freud, science was born of man's inner unhappiness.

Marxist sociologists, on the other hand, trying to provide a historical materialist explanation for the rise of science in the seventeenth century, have not really dissented from the thesis of Protestant asceticism. They have emphasized, to be sure, the primary importance of technological needs, but have not disputed the relevant role of Protestant asceticism as the ideology of the bourgeoisie, and hence, of the rise of science. . . .

There has been a basic agreement, indeed, between the leading sociological schools, the Marxist and the Weberian, as to the significant role of Protestant asceticism. Both schools asserted that there was a functional linkage between the Protestant ethic and the scientific activity of the new bourgeois civilization. While Weber, on the one hand, held that the Protestant ethic was a precondition for the rise of European capitalism and science, Marx said it was, rather, the concurrent consequence of this rise. Yet Marxists and Weberians alike shared the view that the Protestant ascetic ethic somehow made it likely that its adherents would become more effective seekers after scientific truth.

Has this concentration on the Protestant ethic, however, radically misperceived the origins of modern science? Misgivings have persisted. Pitirim Sorokin, in a bypath to his studies of cyclical fluctuations in human history, noted that the scientific contribution of Catholic Italians during the first half of the seventeenth century was higher than that of any other country. This fact alone, he held, would refute the notion that there was a direct causal relationship between the Protestant ethic and the emergence of modern science. Even those who acknowledged that Protestant England had led European science at the end of the seventeenth century were uncertain as to what exactly the alleged connection between Puritanism and science had been. "The influence of Protestantism on natural science," wrote Richard S. Westfall, "is nebulous and difficult to determine." S. Lilley accepted the documentation by Robert Merton and Dorothy Stimson, which purported to prove that Puritan beliefs had been a driving force in the origins of modern science, but both he and

James W. Carroll wondered whether "Protestant" and "Puritan" were being used so loosely as to conceal under their rubric rationalistic, empirical, skeptical, and even atheistic tendencies. Was it possible that two disparate contemporary phenomena were being assigned a relatedness that had never obtained in actuality?

That the scientific revolution was the outcome of a liberation of curiosity all would agree. The question, however, remains unsettled: What was the emotional revolution in seventeenth-century thinkers which turned them into men of science? What was the psychological revolution upon which the scientific revolution was founded? Modern science, writes Lynn White, Jr., as it first appeared in the later Middle Ages, "was one result of a deep-seated mutation in the general attitude toward nature." The new science, he continues, was an aspect "of an unprecedented yearning for immediate experience of concrete facts which appears to have been characteristic of the waxing third estate." What, then, was the character of this deep-seated emotional mutation? What changes in attitude and feeling toward human thought, sensation, and knowledge made possible the emergence of scientific intellectuals?

Certainly there are strong antecedent grounds for doubting that Protestant asceticism would have nurtured the spirit of science. The Calvinist doctrine of original sin was plainly hostile to the pretension of ordinary human beings to understand the world. For the Fall of Adam and Eve, according to the Calvinist, so corrupted their descendants' faculties and senses as to destroy their natural powers for knowing the world. It was a consequence of the ascetic Protestant standpoint, as Paul H. Kocher writes, that "all science was false, and would continue to be so, except as God rescued it by giving to chosen individuals at chosen times a special grace to discover the truth.". . .

Myth and fantasy can infiltrate the perception of even great social scientists, and the consistent scheme of Weber's hypothesis may also consistently misrepresent the origins of science.

In this study, I shall try to show that the scientific intellectual was born from the hedonist-libertarian spirit which, spreading through Europe in the sixteenth and seventeenth centuries, directly nurtured the liberation of human curiosity. Not asceticism, but satisfaction; not guilt, but joy in the human status; not self-abnegation, but self-affirmation; not original sin, but original merit and worth; not gloom, but merriment; not contempt for one's body and one's senses, but delight in one's physical being; not the exaltation of pain, but the hymn to pleasure — this was the emotional basis of the scientific movement of the seventeenth century. Herbert Butterfield has spoken of "a certain dynamic quality" which entered into Europe's "secularization of thought" in the seventeenth century. What I shall try to show is how the hedonist-libertarian ethic provided the momentum for the scientific revolution, and was in fact the creed of the emerging movements of scientific intellectuals everywhere.

VARIETIES OF HEDONISTIC AND ASCETIC ETHICS

What do we mean by the "hedonistic ethic"? What likewise is meant by the phrase "ascetic ethic," or "Protestant ethic" in Weber's sense? Basically, an ethic is hedonist when it is free from a sense of primal guilt; a hedonist outlook is characterized by an absence of internalized self-aggression. "Good" can then be defined in terms of the person's spontaneous likings and desires. The Calvinist ethic, in which the asceticism of the sixteenth and seventeenth centuries was expressed, was founded by contrast on an assertion of the primacy of guilt. . . .

The Calvinist philosophy was a metaphysics of guilt; it held that man is a creature born in original sin, pervaded by sin, maimed by sin; with St. Augustine, Calvin declares that "the naturall giftes were corrupted in man by sinne." Repentance was

man's primary virtue; his salvation could come only through God's grace. The Calvinist ethic was permeated with hatred of the body, hatred of the senses and pleasure. Man's desire for pleasure had brought his fall; austerity, frugality, self-denial were good because they mortified the fount of man's sin.

Now, there are various types of asceticism, as there are different kinds of hedonism. Asceticism has taken different forms under different historical conditions. By and large, however, we can distinguish two principal varieties of asceticism, the first of which we may call "utilitarian asceticism" and the second "masochistic asceticism."

The utilitarian ascetic is a person who forgoes an immediate pleasure in order to have a greater one in the future. The pioneers who endured the hardships of the American frontier were utilitarian ascetics; they looked forward to the enjoyments of the future, when their houses would be built, when their fields would be under cultivation, and they would know the blessings of peace and prosperity. Pains, deprivations, frustrations were undergone not for their own sake but because they would make possible more of pleasures, life's goods, in the future. The masochistic ascetic, however, has come to value pain for its own sake. He is punishing himself. From the domain of his unconscious, a harsh, cruel tyrant condemns any spontaneous desire he may have for pleasurable experience. The masochistic ascetic acquiesces to the will of the unconscious authority, his superego. His self-punitive asceticism is the outcome of an identification with or submission of the absolute superego, and this internalized self-aggression issues in self-reproach, in spiritual groveling, in humility, in torments of anxiety and guilt. Within the unconscious, the longing for joy persists; on the level of overt action, however, the masochistic ascetic has become a seeker after pain. The psychological revolution which made possible the birth of modern science consisted precisely in the overcoming by an intellectual elite in

Western Europe of masochistic asceticism.

It is also useful to distinguish between the asceticism which is mother-centered and that which is father-centered. The Roman Catholic ascetics were typically mother-centered; from St. Augustine on, they were dominated by loyalty to their mother — which they combined with a rejection of other women. The mother, in the symbolic person of the Virgin Mary, was progressively purified of any sexual impurity; the father was allowed to recede into the background, and the ascetic fulfilled a son's loyalty to the mother. "The amount of attention and significance given the Virgin Mary, the mother of Christ," writes W. Lloyd Warner, "is a crucial test of what it means to be a Catholic or a Protestant. . . . The role of the pure virgin and the saintly mother, combined in the figure of one woman, creates a symbol of ideal simplicity to arouse and evoke the deep oedipus love of all males. . . . The love for their own mother is contained and bound by the worship of virginity."

The Protestant ascetic, on the other hand, is father-centered and dominated by a strong superego figure. The father frowns on the terminology of love; he prefers the language of fear, and prizes the "God-fearing man." William Jennings Bryan, an exemplar of American fundamentalism, was an ideal type of Protestant ascetic in his upbringing and in his attitude to science. Bryan's father, a Baptist, would often stop work at noon to hear his son read him a chapter from the Bible; then they would discuss it. His virtues were always those his father had taught. Religious uncertainties crossed through Bryan's mind in his adolescence, but he surmounted them by identification with his father and teachers. He was always grateful, he wrote, to his Christian instructors, under whose guidance "the doubts aroused by my studies were resolved by putting them beside a powerful and loving God." Parental authority in Bryan was strengthened at this critical time against the threat of scientific method, and he went on to become the doughty champion of American ascetic Protestantism against modern science.

Both the mother-centered and father-centered varieties of asceticism, with different emphases, are hostile to the scientific spirit. It does not follow, however, that every form of hedonism is cordial to it. Confucius, for instance, approved of pleasure-seeking through listening to music, being with one's friends, and discussing moral excellence. He was an empiricist; he rejected any claim to innate knowledge, and refused to discuss questions concerning the supernatural. But his hedonism was authoritarian rather than libertarian, and, as such, was constrained within a demarcated domain. . . .

The hedonist-libertarian ethic, on the other hand, includes that ingredient which makes for what Francis Galton simply called "independence of character." In his classical study on the sociology of English scientists in the nineteenth century, Galton observed, "The home atmosphere which the scientific men breathed in their youth was generally saturated with the spirit of independence.". . .

The menace of a stern religious or authoritarian superego was strikingly absent among the English scientists. As far as their religious beliefs were concerned, wrote Galton, "they seem singularly careless of dogma, and exempt from mysterious terror." Piety, the "dependent frame of mind," as Galton called it, was not a trait of the scientists' characters. He noted, furthermore, that "few of the sons of clergymen" were to be found on his list of scientists, a remarkable fact when we remember to what a large extent the universities of England in the nineteenth century were devoted to training young men in divinity.

This freedom from an authoritarian superego, so typical among Victorian men of science, was likewise an essential constituent in the hedonist ethic which nourished the childhood of modern science. The hedonist-libertarian ethic thus involves an individualistic emphasis, in the sense that the individual does not feel himself enthralled by some cultural censor. This new scientific individualism was abhorred by those who, like Martin Luther, regarded with affright the prospect of a continuous revision of received opinions by successive generations of independent thinkers. "Whoever wants to be clever," wrote Luther sardonically against the scientific individualists, "must needs produce something of his own, which is bound to be the best since *he* has produced it."

The greatest original scientific thinkers, we might say, are persons whose thought has remained incompletely "socialized." Einstein once described himself vividly:

I have never belonged wholeheartedly to any country or state, to my circle of friends, or even to my own family. . . .

This libertarian trait was shared by such thinkers as Newton, Freud, and Darwin. The sociological theory of knowledge has usually failed to do justice to this asocial element in creative thought. . . .

There were four ways in which the makers of the scientific revolution adhered to a standpoint more hedonistic, more expressive of their underlying human desires.

First, the new scientists found a direct joy and pleasure in scientific activity itself. The source of scientific creativity has always been a spirit of play, not of work. In play, the free imagination leaps out of customary channels, delighting in novelty, so that it is filled with an exhilaration, an excitement. When Einstein described the inwardness of his thinking, he said it was a kind of "combinatory play," an "associative play" with images. Such was likewise the spirit of Kepler when he wrote that science was play, akin to God's play, like a child's play, purposeless, but with a simple delight in configuration and form: "As God the Creator played, so He also taught nature, as His image, to play the very game which He played before her." This direct joy in scientific activity, characteristic of the childhood and youth of science, we shall call *immediate* or *expressive hedonism*. . . .

The scientists of the seventeenth century, in addition to being expressive hedonists, were also *utilitarian hedonists*. They claimed that the pursuit of science would alleviate men's toil, rescue them from the curse of drudgery, and ensure to them a more pleasant, civilized existence. Descartes and Leibniz foretold that science opened the prospect of an immense technological advancement for mankind. We can "render ourselves the masters and possessors of nature," wrote Descartes, if in place of the schoolmen's philosophy, we learn the forces and actions of physical bodies "as distinctly as we know the different crafts of our artisans.". . .

Leibniz was from his youth dedicated to projects for the foundation of academies and societies that would stimulate the application of science to manufacture, and would revive the industrial prosperity and scientific leadership that the Thirty Years' War had destroyed in Germany. But it was Francis Bacon who was the outstanding prophet of the utilitarian contribution of science; the Royal Society venerated Bacon, and promised Englishmen in the age of the Merry Monarch, Charles II, that scientific research would make for an even merrier England. . . .

The Baconian conception of science is predominantly that of the utilitarian hedonist; the pursuit of science, apart from its joy in itself, is an instrument for the improvement of the lot of mankind. Insofar as it has an element of direct pleasure, this derives in part from its satisfaction of aggressive drives directed against the environment. The liberation of human energies which it advocated was to be attained by rechanneling internalized self-aggressive energies into externalized aggressive energies. The human race was not to war against itself either in individual asceticism or group destruction; it was to conquer nature. . . .

Though the scientific intellectuals, an emerging community, cooperated on behalf of a common ideal and aim, they were as individuals often intensely competitive. In addition to being expressive and utilitarian, theirs was an *individualistic* hedonism. They abandoned any abnegation of self; they longed to see their own names linked to discoveries; they came to value a this-worldly immortality. So far from regarding it a sin, the scientific intellectuals took frank delight in pride. Henry Oldenburg, the first editor of the *Philosophical Transactions of the Royal Society*, assured Robert Boyle that his journal would carefully record priorities in scientific discovery. . . . Scientists posed problems as challenges for their fellow-scientists, and the competition was keen, sometimes envious. Jacques Bernoulli of Basel, in 1696, challenged the mathematicians of Europe to solve the problem of isoperimetrical figures. He even offered a reward to the solver. Many sought for the solution. Jean Bernoulli, Jacques' brother, claiming erroneously to have the solution, quarreled bitterly with Jacques; then he published Jacques's solution as his own after his brother died — yet Jean was the gifted discoverer of the exponential calculus! Competitive strife over the priority in the discovery of the calculus separated with suspicion and malevolence the greatest of the mathematicians, Newton and Leibniz. A competitive individualism was part, however, of the pride in selfhood which the psychological revolution endorsed.

Lastly, the makers of the scientific revolution found themselves seeking a conception of the universe in which man would be less fear-ridden, less anxiety-surrounded, less open to the terrors of bewildering supernatural agents. . . .

The scientists of the seventeenth century swept away the miserable universe of death, famine, and the torture of human beings in the name of God. They took a world that had been peopled with demons and devils, and that superstition had thronged with unseen terror at every side. They cleansed it with clear words and plain experiment. They found an ethic that advised people to renounce their desires, and to cultivate in a hostile universe the humility which befitted their impotence, and they taught men instead to take pride in their human status, and to dare to change the world into one which would answer more fully to their desires. . . .

The scientific movement in the seventeenth century was not the by-product of an increase of repression or asceticism. It was the outcome of a liberation of energies; it derived from a lightening of the burden of guilt. With the growing awareness that happiness and joy are his aims, man could take frank pleasure in the world around him. Libidinal interests in external objects could develop unthwarted; the world was found interesting to live in — an unending stage for fresh experience. Energies were no longer consumed in inner conflicts. With an awakened respect for his own biological nature, self-hatred was cast off. Empiricism was the expression of a confidence in one's senses; the eyes and ears were no longer evidences of human corruption but trusted avenues to a knowledge of nature. The body was not the tainted seat of ignorance, but the source of pleasures and the means for knowledge. Human energies, hitherto turned against themselves, could reach out beyond concern for exclusive self.

THE ROLE OF ART IN THE SCIENTIFIC RENAISSANCE

GIORGIO DE SANTILLANA

A specialist in the philosophy and sciences of the Renaissance, Giorgio de Santillana (1902–   ) is the author of a modern reappraisal of Galileo's famous dispute with the Catholic Church—*The Crime of Galileo* (1955)—and the editor and annotator of a seventeenth-century translation of Galileo's popular astronomical work the *Dialogue on the Great World Systems* (1953). Few who write on Renaissance science today can match de Santillana's knowledge of the philosophical currents of that era and his sensitive appreciation of Renaissance art and literature. His profound understanding of fifteenth-century Italian culture has led him to seek the origins of modern science in what is certainly one of the most prominent distinguishing features of the Renaissance—its artistic activity.

De Santillana is currently Professor of the History and Philosophy of Science at the Massachusetts Institute of Technology.

WHAT I INTEND TO DO, in this essay, is to concentrate on the early period, which centers around Filippo Brunelleschi (1377–1446). Its importance, I think, has not been sufficiently brought to light. We are here at the initial point where the historian has to unscramble ideas. Brunelleschi around 1400 should be considered the most creative scientist as well as the most creative artist of his time, since there was nothing much else then that could go by the name of creative science.

We must not superimpose our own image of science as a criterion for the past. It is Brunelleschi who seems to define the way of science for his generation. Who was it that gave him his initial scientific ideas? Was it Manetti or, as others suggest, Toscanelli? Or someone else, still? Under what form? A historian of art, Pierre Francastel, has some veiled reproaches against historians of science. "So little is known," he says, "about history of science in that period, that we have no bearings.". . .

We are, then, on the spot, and we had better accept the reminder. We have not yet created our own techniques of analysis in that no man's land between art and science; we have all too few of the facts and none of the critical tools. . . .

Two great issues come to mind when we think of that epoch-making change. One is the rise of the modern concept of natural law over and against the medieval one which applies to society, another the intellectual "change of axes" which allowed an explanation of nature no longer in terms of form but in terms of mathematical function.

On these issues, history of science has not much to say before the time of Galileo and Descartes, except to point up the well-known scholastic attempts. Prophetic utterances are quoted, which, scattered over three centuries, fall short of conclusiveness. We are still looking for where the thing actually *took place* in its first form.

Let us then try to make a landfall at a

point where art and science, undeniably, join. Brunelleschi created his theory of perspective by experimental means. He built the earliest optical instrument after the eyeglasses. We have Manetti's description of the device, a wooden tablet of about half an ell, in which he had painted "with such diligence and excellence and care of color, that it seemed the work of a miniaturist," the square of the Cathedral in Florence, seen from a point three feet inside the main door of the cathedral. What there was of open sky within the painting he had filled in with a plate of burnished silver, "so that the air and sky should be reflected in it as they are, and so the clouds, which are seen moving on that silver as they are borne by the winds." In the front, at the point where the perpendicular of vision met the portrayed scene, he had bored a hole not much bigger than the pupil of the eye, which funnelled out to the other side. Opposite the tablet, at arm's length, he had mounted a mirror. If you looked then, through the hole from the back of the tablet at its reflection in the mounted mirror, you saw the painting exactly from its perspective point, "so that you thought you saw the proper truth and not an image."

The next step, as we see it now, is to invert the device and let in the light through the pinhole, to portray by itself the exterior scene on an oiled paper screen. This is the *camera obscura,* not quite the one that Alberti described for the first time in 1430, but its next of kin, and it took time to be properly understood. But the whole train of ideas originated with Brunelleschi, between 1390 and 1420.

We have thus not *one* device, but a set of experimental devices of enormous import, comparable in importance to that next device which came two centuries later, namely, Galileo's telescope. Galileo, it will be remembered, announced his instrument as derived "from the more recondite laws of perspective," and in their very inappositeness (at least in modern usage), the words are revealing. The new thing could be understood by opinion only as one more

"perspective instrument" and indeed its earliest Latin name was *perspicillum,* whence the English "perspective glass," a name which might apply just as well to Brunelleschi's devices.

We may note that Copernicus himself, untroubled by any modern thought of dynamics, had candidly proposed his system as a proper perspective construction: "Where should the Lamp of the Universe be rightly placed except in the center?" Conversely, there is a "Copernican" spirit about perspective. People will be portrayed as small as they have to be, if they are that distant. There is nothing wrong in looking small if the mind knows the law of proportion; whereas the medieval artists had felt that change of size had to be held within the limits of the symbolic relationship and importance of the figures to the whole.

What the devices of Brunelleschi have done is in every way as significant as the achievement of the telescope. If the telescope established the Copernican system as a physical reality, and gave men an idea of true astronomical space, Brunelleschi's devices went a long way towards establishing in natural philosophy a new idea concerning the nature of light. . . .

Surely, here we have the beginnings of a science — a science of visive rays, as Leonardo calls it, so scientific that there is even an apparatus designed for it. But what is it for? To help us portray rightly what we see around us — essentially, to give the illusion of it. Illusionism is a strong motive, inasmuch as the most direct application is to scenographic design. This in itself is no mean thing, nor merely a way to amuse the rich. It has been proved that those monumental town perspectives — like that of the main square of Urbino by a pupil of Piero — are no mere exercises in drawing, they are actually projects for an architecture that is not yet there, and the first sketches of town planning. This is in the true line of development, for Brunelleschi himself had devised his instrument as an aid to architectural planning. But where does it leave us as far as science is concerned?

George Sarton appraised it crisply in *Six Wings,* his last book on the Renaissance. After giving a brief historical summary on perspective, he concludes: "Linear perspective implied a certain amount of mathematical knowledge, but not a great deal. The best mathematical work was done in other fields, such as trigonometry and algebra." And that's that; or rather, let it stand, even if we are tempted to qualify it. The treatment that Kepler gives in his *Optics* to just such constructions, involving catoptrics, shows the thing to require no inconsiderable mathematical skill. The point remains that Sarton considers the subject not particularly important.

Yet we all agree that if the history of science is to be understood as George Sarton himself wanted it understood, a dominant cultural factor, we cannot push it off again at such a critical juncture to a couple of algebraists working in a corner. . . . The Scientific Revolution should be seen and studied as a major intellectual mutation, which obviously started about the time when both interest and relevance seemed to have slipped out from under the scholastic system without anyone being able to say why. . . . Beyond the mass of heterogeneous social factors, the rise of this and the decline of that, which are strung together in the common histories, what do we know about the actual "replacing" element? The shift of opinion can be traced to the early Renaissance. It cannot be accounted for by still non-existent experimental results, nor by "industrial growth," nor, even less, by any advances in trigonometry. That is why research seems to center at present on the new interest among scholars for the mathematical "method." I submit that, valuable as it is, it is not the answer, and I hope later on to show that indeed it could provide no "replacement.". . .

Much, of course, has been written about perspective by cultural historians. It has been said, authoritatively, that Quattrocento painting places man inside a world, the real world, exactly portrayed according to physical laws, that it asserts naturalism against medieval symbolism, and thus creates the natural presupposition for science. This may be very rightly said, but one goes on feeling uncomfortable. Such a piling up of obvious factors until science is then produced out of a hat looks suspicious. . . . Even more does it behoove us to be careful in dealing with large words like "naturalism." There is surely full-blown naturalism in Leonardo, but he expresses it mainly by being a natural philosopher: There the ambiguity is lifted. For he certainly *is* a natural philosopher. . . .

The problem may become clearer if we think of the second stage, so much more familiar to us. Two centuries later, at the time of Galileo, the struggle between the old and the new form of knowledge is out in the open. Galileo is an acknowledged master of acknowledged science, in mathematics and in astronomy, yet he has to contend all his life with the prejudice which denies him philosophical status. He is treated as a technician and denied any capacity to deal with the true causes of things, which are of the domain of cosmology, as taught in the schools. We all remember how much persuasion he had to spend to show that when we have found a "necessary," i.e., a mathematical cause, we have as true a cause as the mind can encompass and that we need not look farther afield. We know that it took the combined effort of Galileo, Descartes, and Newton to establish the new idea of a natural philosophy.

If now we come back to 1400 instead of 1600, when the medieval frame of ideas was still an overarching and unchallenged presence, when what we call science was still a hole-and-corner affair without a character of its own, if we think of this group of men who had no connection with the universities, little access to books, who hardly even dressed as burghers and went around girt in the leather apron of their trade—then, I say, it is no use vaguely talking about genius; we have to show some concrete possibilities underlying this sudden creation of a new world of theoretical conceptions.

The period I am referring to is fairly

well defined. It is the fifteenth century it-self; it starts with Brunelleschi's early work; it has reached a conclusion by 1500 with Leonardo and Luca Pacioli.

The first thing was for these men to have some conception of their social role which allowed them to think legitimately. Here we can see that they found an anchoring point in the old theory, reinterpreted. For just as medicine claimed the "physics" of the schools as its patron science (hence the names "physic" and "physician"), those craftsmen had two of the mechanical arts, architecture and *theatrica,* and above those, music and mathematics. By the time of Pollaiolo, it is commonly understood that architecture is a straight liberal art.

But mark the difference. The painter remained with only a mechanical art, *theatrica,* back of him. . . . The architect, instead, has something unequivocally solid to handle. He builds reality.

This leads up to the *third* factor, the new type of patronage from a new ruling class. It is significant that just about the time when Brunelleschi was called in as a consultant to the Opera del Duomo (the Works Committee for the Cathedral) its last ecclesiastical members were dropped and it became an entirely lay body: Brunelleschi on his side, once he is the executive, shows a new technocratic high-handedness in firing the master builders *en masse* for obstructionism and re-hiring them on his own terms. . . .

Here we have, then, for the first time the Master Engineer of a new type, backed by the prestige of mathematics and of the "recondite secrets of perspective" (Galileo's tongue-in-cheek description of his own achievements is certainly valid here), the man whose capacity is not supposed to depend only on long experience and trade secrets, but on strength of intellect and theoretical boldness, who derides and side-steps the usual thinking-by-committee, who can speak his mind in the councils of the city and is granted patents for his engineering devices. . . . He is, in fact, the first professional engineer as opposed to the old and tradition-bound figure of the "master builder.". . . But still and withal, he is acknowledged to the end of his life as the great designer and artist; not only that, but as the man who masters the philosophical implications of what he is doing. Donatello may be acquainted with the Latin classics; he is still considered a craftsman. Brunelleschi is not; he stands as an intellectual. It is only a century later that the fateful distinction emerges between pure and applied art. By that time, the pure artist himself is hardly an intellectual.

Finally, we have the fact that this complex of achievements by a well-led group of great talents — Manetti, Ghiberti, Donatello, Masaccio, Uccello, Luca della Robbia, with Brunelleschi as leader — found a literary expounder of comparable talent in the person of Leon Battista Alberti (d. 1472) who gave their ideas full citizenship in the robed world of letters and humanism — something that only Galileo was able later to achieve by himself. It will have been a fragile and fleeting conjunction, no doubt. By insisting on a "science of beauty" Alberti perpetuated the rigidity of medieval disciplines with their ancient idea of "methods," and their dictation of what is right. It will end up in mere academism, about the time when science breaks forth with its own idea of method and of truth. But as long as it lasted, in the period of creation, it has been a true conjunction, both in one. Alberti only paraphrases Filippo's words (we know that) when he says of the new art of architecture: "If it ever was written in the past, we have dug it up, and if it was not, we have drawn it from heaven." That "social breakthrough" that the new science of Galileo effected through the telescope, we find here in its early counterpart or rather first rehearsal. . . .

We have lined up, one, two, three, four, the preconditions, or what our dialectical colleagues would call the objective possibilities for a scientific renascence, as well as, I daresay, the proper revolutionary consciousness; yet, even if we go and comb the patent records in approved dialectical style, we shall not be able to register the birth of modern empirical science. We are left with the question we started out with: "What was it? In the name of what?"...

What the revolution was about is less easy to define, because of the intellectually elusive quality of art. Such a theory as the Copernican will put the issue squarely, as between closed world and infinite universe. It will bring violent reactions and counteractions beyond the bounds of reason.... Whereas the artist simply projects the thing, something that stands there by itself, he brings in magically a new way of seeing, and then leaves imagination to take its course. What comes out in this case, for instance, is that when the artistic revolution is done, all the old emotions about realism and nominalism are as dead as a door nail. Something new is in the world, but the creators have gone unchallenged....

It is then left to us to decide what the new thing actually *is,* and to evaluate it. This will be the subject of the last part of this paper.

It might be well to see first what they *thought* it was. The literary theorist of the movement is Leon Battista Alberti, himself an artist of sufficient stature to assure us that he understood what his friends were about. The label that he puts on it is the neoplatonic one. Neoplatonism was orthodox enough to be safe, strong and speculative enough to be new. The mathematical bent of the whole school was so marked, that such a label is hardly unexpected. Here again, we are faced with the fact so well marked by Professor Koyré, that the new thought arising against the old logic is of a necessity under the invocation of Plato, and will stay so until and after Galileo. The Galilean way in dynamics, as he points out, is to explain the real case by way of a theoretical one that can never be brought under observation, the concrete by way of the abstract, what *is* by way of what cannot be said to "be."

The theory of linear perspective might seem too simple to lend itself to such weighty thoughts. It can be kept down to a workout in elementary geometry, just as Sarton described it, and one wonders why the medievals who tried found such difficulties in relating the objects portrayed to a fixed position — if it is really a matter of drawing lines. But let us not forget that Alberti, like most theoreticians, is putting his new wine in old bottles, whence the label of Platonism. He can use only then-known, i.e., elementary terms, hence his explanation falls short of what is really the case. What we call "a system of mental representation," and "the ordering of a conventional space in depth," and so on, are things which cannot be expressed in his language but only pointed up to. The system that is being evolved is part mathematical, part symbolic and mythical; it is fully there only in the actual works of the artists....

Let us restate the thing in Alberti's simple terms. There is a science, perspective, whose aim is correct comparison and proportion, projection in a visual space (we shall see later all that this implies, but Alberti himself need not be aware of it as yet). It allows us, by way of geometric properties, to deal with the object, the substance, architecture itself, or rather *il murare,* as they say so much more concretely, the *act* of raising walls brick by brick. The right walls. If they know what they are doing, that is all they need....

By transforming the concept of substance into something which could be designed and built up through their science of proportion, the mathematical artists have crossed the otherwise unmanageable distance between Substance and Function. Any attempt at bridging it directly by philosophy would have led to an intellectual impasse, worse, to a breakdown....

Shall we try to describe what we called the fallout, as it seeps in invisibly, all around, for generations before the birth of Galileo?

The new science around 1430 is, as we have concluded, operational in character; that is, it defines the object of its quest by what it does about it, with the difference that whereas the modern object is the experimental procedure, its object is *il mu-*

rare, the building procedure. It remains now to work out its theoretical structure, which is far-ranging.

The peculiar "substance" of that quest is a system of planes and volumes rigorously thought out by way of its properties, known and understood geometrically, physically, functionally, aesthetically, and even symbolically. It imports a fullness of knowledge. The perceptual raw material, as it were, of that knowledge is provided by the past of civilization, for it is in the traditional architecture which is already around, on which judgment and criticism have been able to sharpen themselves. That is the stuff which is now going to be transformed. . . .

Let us make this a little clearer. Form, here, for the artist, has the function of *ratio* or cause of all the species, insofar as there are not really many aspects or forms, but *the* form or the Idea ("concetto"), given by draftsmanship. Perspective shows us the actual size of a thing that looks small in the distance; its position in space determines the truth and invariance of the individual object; its projection the true form abiding in it. The module and reality of the particular are shifted from the thing to geometric space. It is in this space of *ratios* that true construction takes place.

I am trying to paraphrase as best I can the actual ideas of a contemporary who thought he saw what was taking place but could perceive only a dim outline. You cannot expect it to be as clear as a theorem. But if this goes as Platonism, it is certainly not the literary variety with its fashionable uplift. We are treated to diagrams and visual pyramids, to a coördinates net on a screen. We are asked to see longitudinal perspective in terms of that other inverted pyramid ending in the flight-point placed on the infinite circle: that mathematical point at infinity in which all the forms and ratios of reality are absorbed or rather "contracted." . . .

Have I been trying, then, to read philosophy or science into art, a thing reproved both by the scientist and by the aestheti-cian? I trust I have not. We have only to read Alberti to realize these men's keen awareness of their intellectual quest. At a time when what *we* mean by science was still beyond the horizon, when the *name* of science was monopolized by scholastic officials, who officially denied to mathematics any link with physical reality, these men had conceived of an original prototype of science based on mathematics, which was to provide them with a creative knowledge of reality, repeat — creative, and could claim the name of true knowledge in that it dealt with first and last things. There should be some proper way of placing this attempt, in its true dimensions, inside the history of science, but it has yet to be made. . . .

I trust it is plain by now that what is involved in this story are the great categories of scientific philosophy. Erwin Panofsky has characterized the space of classical art as "aggregative." There would have been no better way to describe the space of Aristotle himself, which is nothing but an orderly pile of containers. This common-sensical kind of space is, for a modern, utterly irrelevant. The space of the Renaissance Panofsky describes by contrast as "homogeneous." . . .

Space is for the new imagination a matrix for infinite potential complexities and states and tensions — a matrix awaiting total structure, rather, a manifold of structures. It is on its way to becoming what is for Newton the organ of perception of God, for Malebranche the only intelligible reality, for the theory of central forces the carrier of that incomprehensible property, action at a distance; it is rich enough to bring forth set theory, group transformations, phase spaces, the electromagnetic ether, Riemann's geometry, and the Einsteinian reduction of all reality to properties of the time-space continuum.

To sum up, this investigation seems to suggest that two of the major features of the Scientific Renaissance, namely, the change-over from Form to Function, and the rise of a "natural law" unconnected with the affairs of human society, have their origin in a specific transformation of the arts. They cannot be said to arise out of the scholar's interest in mathematics, which remains wishful, nor out of the development of the crafts per se, nor out of any statistical accumulation of small interactions between the two zones. They are coherently worked out and brought to bear at the time when the representative and building arts form a new idea of themselves, and go through a theoretical elaboration of that new idea, in such a way as to be able to bring it to grips with reality in their crea-

tion. This seems to be the moment when the actual shaping of a new operative thought takes place, and it provides some fundamental categories for nascent scientific thought.

I have barely sketched out the outline of the problem. The analytical tools have yet to be forged. The scientist and the historian of art have hardly ever met, and even then under a cloud of misunderstanding. I am only trying to enter a plea for collaboration in a subject which is still tricky and most difficult.

THE CHEMICAL PHILOSOPHY
OF THE RENAISSANCE

ALLEN G. DEBUS

Trained as a research chemist, historian, and historian of science, Allen G. Debus (1926–   ) has concentrated his research on sixteenth- and seventeenth-century science. He is a frequent contributor to many journals in the field, including *Ambix* (journal of the history of alchemy and early chemistry), the editor of a seventeenth-century collection of English alchemical works— E. Ashmole's *Theatrum Chemicum Britannicum*, and the author of a book-length study of the English followers of the Swiss alchemist Paracelsus. His study of English Paracelsism is important for its revelation of the interconnections between medicine, chemistry, and philosophy in the sixteenth and seventeenth centuries.

Debus is Associate Professor of the History of Science at the University of Chicago.

CHEMISTRY PRIOR TO THE TIME of Robert Boyle has always been an uncertain quantity in assessments of the Scientific Revolution. If on occasion alchemy has been equated with proto-chemistry, it has been more often dismissed as one of mankind's maddest delusions. If anything

it would seem that this latter tendency has been accentuated by historians of science in recent years. Herbert Butterfield perhaps summed up the views of the majority when he wrote that commentators on alchemy "seem to become tinctured with the kind of lunacy they set out to describe." In reaction

Reprinted from an unpublished manuscript entitled "The Chemical Philosophy of the Renaissance." This essay was first presented to the Society of Medical History of Chicago on March 9, 1966. An expanded, annotated version was first published as a pamphlet by the William Andrews Clark Memorial Library (Los Angeles, 1966) and then altered and printed in its final form in *Ambix*, Vol. XIV, no. 1, February 1967, pp. 42–59, under the title: "Renaissance Chemistry and the Work of Robert Fludd." By permission of the author.

to the vagaries of mystical authors — and seeking solid achievement rather than symbols, dreams and allegories — a second trend has been to try to extract chemical processes from tracts on the philosophers' stone, to examine in detail the writings of the Paracelsians from the viewpoint of pharmaceutical chemistry, and to emphasize the metallurgical works of the Renaissance as an island of sanity in a sea of occultism.

Cyril Stanley Smith and R. J. Forbes have written that "the assayer excelled the alchemist in all but the desire for a systematized philosophy." Yet this very statement grants to the alchemists considerable importance, for surely the desire for a systematized philosophy is a basic requisite for the advance of science. One cannot deny that a careful analysis of the alchemical texts, the pharmaceutical works and the metallurgical treatises of the Renaissance for their actual chemical content is of profound importance for our knowledge of the growth of science as we know it, but the blanket dismissal of other supposedly "non-scientific" aspects of early chemistry to the realm of occultism, mysticism and magical hocus-pocus does nothing to add to our knowledge of the birth of modern science. The wide-spread appeal of the mystical Renaissance universe as interpreted by the iatrochemists in the period from the death of Paracelsus to 1670 makes it a subject of special concern for historians of science — and historians of medicine — and it deserves more attention than it has customarily received.

In my own research I have been particularly concerned with this chemical-alchemical revival as it fits into the English intellectual scene of the sixteenth and seventeenth centuries. I should note in passing that there was a complex socio-religious background which affected the growth of Paracelsian thought in England at that time, — but in the few minutes I have at my disposal this evening I would like to touch on the meaning of "chemistry" in that era as a clue to the popularity of the subject. For the most part the aims of the chemists

as expressed in the definitions printed in their books are not unexpected. Chemistry is the spagyric art, the art of separating the pure from the impure — again, it is the art of perfecting the imperfect in nature, that is, the art of transmuting impure metals to gold and silver. And as the alchemist is concerned with curing the sick in inanimate nature, so too he is concerned with the preparation of medicines for the ills of mankind.

These were the most common definitions — practical ones which offer alchemy as an art. Yet there was a broader definition as well. Writing in the tradition of the iatrochemical text book authors in 1660, Nicholas LeFèvre divided the study of chemistry into three main branches. One of these was pharmaceutical chemistry — the actual preparation of those chemical remedies which had been prescribed by the chemical physician. On a higher level was the work of the iatrochemist himself who utilized theory in conjunction with practical knowledge to prescribe the chemical medicine which would cure his patient. Above these divisions, however, LeFèvre placed Philosophical Chemistry whose high priests were Paracelsus and Basil Valentine in the past, and van Helmont and Glauber in his own day. He states:

Chymistry is nothing else but the Art and Knowledge of Nature it self; that it is by her means we examine the Principles, out of which natural bodies do consist and are compounded; and by her are discovered unto us the causes of their sources of their generations and corruptions, and of all the changes and alterations to which they are liable. . . .

In short, the Chemical Philosopher thinks of this science as the "true Key of Nature."

Such claims derive ultimately from traditional alchemy. Centuries earlier Bonus of Ferrara had spoken of alchemy as "the key of all good things, the Art of Arts, the Science of Sciences," while the pseudo-Lullian treatise *Incipit Practica super lapide philosophico* begins with a sweeping definition of alchemy. Not only was the alchemist to be concerned with the purification of metals and driving forth illness from man, — the author goes on:

Sons, this science is called *flos regalis* through which the human intellect is rectified through the force of experience with respect to the eyes and true observation since its experiments cannot suffer phantastic proofs, and rather it gives a vivid entrance to the intellect to *all other sciences* [my ital. AGD] since it has divine virtues to penetrate those truths which are veiled. . . .

Broad definitions such as these are not uncommon in Medieval Latin texts, but the same works were devoted primarily to the search for the philosophers' stone and it is for the most part in the 16th and 17th centuries that we see a sincere effort to view all of nature as a vast chemical laboratory. In great measure the Paracelsians were responsible for this. Paracelsus had insisted that alchemy gave us an "adequate explanation of the properties of all the four elements" — meaning thereby that alchemy has as its province the study of the whole cosmos. It was this broad meaning of the word which his followers referred to when they spoke of the chemical philosophy. In England R. Bostocke explained in 1585 that true medicine is nothing other than "the searching out of the secretes of nature," and this is to be carried out by resort to "mathematicall and supernaturall precepts, the exercise whereof is Mechanicall, and to be accomplished with labor." Thus, medicine was equated with our science, but Bostocke went on to state that the real name for all of this was simply chemistry or alchemy. Other theoretical Paracelsians and mystical alchemists such as Peter Severinus, Oswald Croll, Michael Maier and Robert Fludd took much the same line — natural phenomena might best be interpreted through chemical studies or analogies, and true medicine is essentially nothing but chemistry.

There was a deep religious significance connected with the chemical philosophy. As devout Christians the Paracelsians believed strongly in the two-fold revelation of the Lord. Commenting on this Thomas Tymme (c. 1550–c. 1610) wrote:

The Almighty Creatour of the Heauens and the Earth, (Christian Reader), hath set before our eyes two most principall Bookes: the one of Nature, the other of his written Word. . . . The wisedome of Natures booke men commonly call Naturall Philosophie, which serueth to allure to the contemplation of that great and incomprehensible God, that wee might glorifie him in the greatnesse of his worke. For the ruled motions of the Orbes . . . the connexion, agreement, force, vertue, and beauty of the Elements . . . are so many sundry natures and creatures in the world, are so many interpreters to teach us, that God is the efficient cause of them, and that he is manifested in them, and by them, as their finall cause to whom also they tend.

Indeed, we need the book of nature to understand divinity. If man had not sinned, nature itself would have been enough for man's knowledge of his Creator, but since the Fall of man, "God hath given us his sacred Booke, by meanes whereof, as also by his holy spirit, he communicateth to us as much heauenly light as is needfull for the knowledge of our selues, and of his high Maiestie."

The implication is clear, to understand his Creator man may obtain truth both through the Holy Scriptures or through some mystical religious experience, and through his diligent study of Nature, God's book of Creation. At all events, the "heathnish" Aristotelian and Galenic teachings of the Schools must be rejected and the Universities themselves must be reformed to accommodate this new Christian learning.

The almost evangelistic zeal of the Paracelsians toward fresh observations and experiments is characteristic of them. Although this derives in part from their alchemical heritage, it is nevertheless true that they were strong supporters of the call for a new and unprejudiced investigation of nature. Pyrotechny became their key to this knowledge — the anonymous author of the *Philiatros* (1615) joyously exhorted his readers to "put then on Glouves and Cuffes, for you must to the fire, and happily to the fiery Furnace." Peter Severinus, the revered Danish Paracelsian philosopher, urged all true physicians to:

sell your lands, your houses, your garments and your jewelry; burn up your books. On the other hand, buy yourselves stout shoes, travel to the mountains, search the valleys, the deserts, and the shores of the sea, and the deepest depressions of the earth; note with care the distinctions between animals, the differences of plants, the various kinds of minerals, the properties and mode of origin of everything that exists. Be not ashamed to study diligently the astronomy and terrestrial philosophy of the peasantry. Lastly, purchase coal, build furnaces, watch and operate with the fire without wearying. In this way and no other, you will arrive at a knowledge of things and their properties.

These men prided themselves on their independent investigations. Rejecting the current philosophical debate on the different element systems in the mid-1580s, Thomas Moffett scornfully commented that:

Some wish that there should be but one element, while others think there are many, and some even think they are infinite, innumerable and immovable: these assert that there are two, those three, some others say four, while others still demand eight.

But for Moffett, the Paracelsians were in a different class. For them the body of man (and therefore all created things if man is to be considered a true microcosm) "consists of sulphur, mercury, and salt alone, not because we know this as perfectly as Adam, but because the actual resolution of all kinds of natural as well as artificial bodies shows it to be so."

On the surface the Paracelsians' rejection of traditional learning and their definition of chemistry as an experimental, mathematical and mechanical investigation of nature sounds remarkably modern. Yet, what was this chemical philosophy based upon? We find a substructure of Hermetic, Pythago-

rean and neo-Platonic thought. Essential to all orthodox Paracelsian theorists was the macrocosm-microcosm analogy — a scheme still so widely accepted in the 16th century that it was seldom felt necessary to defend it. One need only cite the *Emerald Table* of Hermes or a host of other revered authors — or perhaps cite the innumerable signs or signatures which seemed to link heaven and earth. In the *Triumphal Chariot of Antimony* Basil Valentine offers a typical alchemical "dream sequence" in which he affirms that he ascended on high and in so doing viewed the whole universe and proved the correspondence of the macrocosm and the microcosm — yet in general this was a truth accepted by everyone which seemed to require no formal proof.

Also deriving from Hermetic sources was the emphasis on the Biblical story of Creation. Here the most commonly cited Paracelsian source is the *Philosophy to the Athenians*. In it the Creation is interpreted essentially as a divine chemical separation in which special emphasis is placed on the elements from which all other substances derive. In the *Philosophy to the Athenians* the discussion centers primarily around the traditional Aristotelian elements — other authors such as Joseph Duchesne interpret the same text from the viewpoint of the three principles.

If the Creation reduced to a chemical process, it seemed not improper to conclude that nature must continue to operate in chemical terms. Reflecting this viewpoint, LeFèvre observed that "Chymistry makes all natural things, extracted by the omnipotent hand of God, in the Creation, out of the Abysse of the Chaos, her proper and adequate object." The relationship of the two worlds played an important part here. The created universe was conceived to be relatively small with all of its parts interconnected. In his Paracelsian apology Oswald Croll concentrated on this "divine Analogy of this visible World and Man." He affirmed that:

Heaven and Earth are Mans Parents, out of

which Man last of all was created; he that knowes the parents, and can Anatomize them, hath attained the true knowledge of their child man, the most perfect creature in all his properties; because all things of the whole Universe meet in him as in the Centre, and the Anatomy of him in his Nature is the Anatomy of the whole world. . . .

Similarly Elias Ashmole observed that "*Iudiciall Astrologie* is the *Key* of *Naturall Magick,* and *Naturall Magick* the *Doore* that leads to this *Blessed* Stone." In other words, the study of the heavens is the key to natural magic which he defines as Natural or Mathematical Philosophy — and this in turn is the key to the highest science, Alchemy.

The Paracelsians called for observation and experiment — but in relation to a preconceived belief in the unified macrocosm and microcosm. Severinus had insisted that the true physician must learn the dispositions of the elements, the times of the rising and setting of the stars, the periods of the planets, the origins of the comets and the winds, of thunder and lightning, of rains, the differences of animals, metals and minerals. Only after learning all of these things — and many others — will he properly see the correspondences between nature and supernature. The chemical philosophers interpreted their observations from a chemical viewpoint. The formation of the earth's crust could seemingly be duplicated in chemical flasks, mountain streams were to be explained in terms of earthly distillations, thunder and lightning were no less than the explosion of an aerial sulphur and niter duplicating gunpowder on a grand scale, and the rains were due to macrocosmic circulations that imitated the heating of water in the alchemical pelican. But the Paracelsians were physicians and that which interested them most was the relation of all this to man, the microcosm.

As an example of this we might look at the work of Joseph Duchesne who, after considering the formation of meteors, turned immediately to analogous formations in the microcosm. Vapors and exhalations rising from the lower regions to the brain become condensed in the same way that clouds and rain form on the earth. In mild form the result may be a cold with a running nose — in more violent form a more serious disabling of the body. In any case, he concludes, such investigations will teach us the true source of the winds, sleet and snow on the macrocosmic level and of ringing in the ears, paralepsy and apoplexy on the microcosmic level since in all these cases the ultimate cause is the congealing of mercurial vapors by a sudden cooling effect.

An even more interesting example dates from a half century later. Johann Rudolf Glauber makes the following statement:

Seeing therefore, that the constant Circulation of the Blood in the *Microcosm,* can be in no wise deny'd, why should not also such a Circulation in the *Macrocosm* be admitted as true? For as the Blood of the Human Body arising from the Liver, diffuseth it self through all the Passages and Veins of the Body, as well small as great, and Conserveth the life of the whole, nourisheth all the parts, and augmenteth the good juices, which are changed into Flesh, Bones, Skin, and Hairs in the Members themselves, and leaving the unprofitable Phlegm to be expelled by the pores of the skin: So also is it with the Nutriment and Universal Aliment of the great World, while the Salt water without intermission, of the great Sea, or Ocean, encompassing the whole Globe of the Earth, by many small and great passages of Veins, passeth through all the parts of the Earth, and nourisheth and sustaineth them with its Salt, that Minerals, Metals, Stones, Sand, Clay, Shrubs, Trees, and Grass may be nourished and grow, and in growing take their encrease. The rest of the Water being freed from all Saltness, is exterminated as a superfluity in the Superficies, and being diffused into various Springs, as well small as great, is expelled, no otherwise than the superfluous sweat of the Blood in the *Microcosm,* by innumerable passages and pores.

Here, writing a generation after Harvey's great work, an author often referred to as one of the major chemists of the seventeenth century finds the new discoveries only strengthen his belief in the macrocosm-microcosm analogy. And again, what we learn by observation will have a two-fold meaning on the macrocosmic and microcosmic levels.

By the opening of the 17th century Oswald Croll felt that Paracelsus' dream of overturning the ancient doctrines of the schools was imminent if not yet quite achieved. He pointed out that the courts of Europe did not lack competent Paracelsians, and quoting one of them, Albertus Wimpeneus, he argued that the Paracelsian views had triumphed because of the success of their chemical hypotheses, because of the inherent progress of medical knowledge — and finally, because of the simplicity and truth of the macrocosm-microcosm analogy. Yet, it was the excessive and unfounded use of mystical chemical analogies plus the macrocosm-microcosm relationship which brought forth some of the earliest and harshest criticism of the Paracelsians. Many natural philosophers, influenced enough either by Paracelsian or earlier alchemical thought to be loosely classed as Paracelsians themselves, strongly protested against the chemical philosophers whose interests seemed to run more to hypotheses than to experiments. Early in the century Andreas Libavius and Daniel Sennert represent this approach, and to a degree their position was not far removed from that of their contemporary, Francis Bacon, who also lauded the observations of the chemists, but rejected their far-flung hypotheses — and he particularly cited the alleged correspondence of the macrocosm and the microcosm.

In short, a new type of chemical philosopher was developing in the 17th century. In a sense van Helmont typifies this newer breed. By his own admission strongly influenced by the writings of Paracelsus, he nevertheless continually objected to the mysticism of his hypotheses. Van Helmont writes:

The name of Microcosm or little World is Poetical, heathenish, and metaphorical, but not natural, or true. It is likewise a Phantastical, hypochondriacal and mad thing, to have brought all the properties, and species of the universe into man, and the art of healing.

Yet, though specific Paracelsian views might be condemned such as the macrocosm-microcosm analogy, the similarities between the outlook and goal of van Helmont and the Paracelsians seem to outweigh the differences. In the same tradition van Helmont felt that medicine was the chief end of natural philosophy. And while he might willingly give "mathematical demonstrations" — by which he meant manual experiments — a strictly mathematical method for him was akin to logic and therefore smacked of Aristotelianism. Mathematics might and should be used for calculations and measurements, but it was not basic to science. Rather, "the Philosopher . . . is never admitted to the Root, or radical knowledge of natural things, without the fire." Van Helmont and his followers emphasized observation and experiment in the Paracelsian-alchemical tradition, but at the same time they were willing to explain physiological and earthly processes in chemical terms often on a basis no more firmly grounded than those of the mystical alchemists they rejected.

The Helmontian restatement of Paracelsism stressing experimentalism and allegedly stripped of baseless hpyotheses found many supporters in the mid-17th century. It had a natural appeal for physicians interested in the new philosophy since it was openly experimental in approach and it stressed medicine as the chief goal of natural philosophy. At the same time those who found chemical interpretations more appealing than mathematical abstractions were being offered a path to true knowledge — not of just one branch of science, but, again in Paracelsian tradition, of all nature. In R. F. Jones' *Ancients and Moderns* a survey of the English literature shows that an impressive number of mid-17th century reformers were advocating the study of spagyric chemistry as a replacement for the traditional Aristotelian road to nature. Noah Biggs was expressing a fairly common view when he wrote:

. . . wherein do they (the universities) contribute to the promotion or discovery of Truth? . . . Where have we any thing to do with Mechanick *Chymistrie* the handmaid of Nature, that hath outstript the other Sects of Philosophie, by her multiplied real experiences? . . .

For Robert Boyle, van Helmont was "a benefactor to experimental learning" and he lamented the fact that the chemists were thought to have brought forth so many experiments in support of their views:

that of those that have quitted the unsatisfactory Philosophy of the Schools, the greater Number dazzl'd as it were by the Experiments of Spagyrists, have imbrac'd their Doctrines instead of those they deserted.

Boyle proposed to offer experiments which would lure these disenchanted Aristotelians to the Mechanical Philosophy.

Indeed, the third quarter of the 17th century did see a resurgence of interest in the chemical philosophy—now perhaps more genuinely experimental than the Paracelsian universe of a century earlier, but it remained an approach with still the same goals. These men still spoke not narrowly of technical applications of chemistry, but of a true understanding of nature

through the aid of chemical theories based on laboratory investigations. Like the mechanical philosophers, the Paracelsians and the Helmontians stood for an unyielding attack on the blind authority of the ancients. Like the mechanical philosophers they insisted that the secrets of nature would only unfold through an unyielding observational and experimental approach — and like them, they claimed that their method would yield eventually the secrets of the universe. That they were wrong is not the main issue here. What is important is that they strove for the same goals as the mechanical philosophers — and they were encouraged to do so by hypotheses and analogies which we today would reject outright. It seems to me that if we are to understand the 16th and 17th century mechanical philosophers, astronomers, and mathematicians who showed evidence at one time or another of an interest in traditional alchemy or any other phase of chemistry, we should be willing to at least consider the possibility that this interest may stem not necessarily from a desire on their part to transmute the base metals to gold — or even to apply corpuscular philosophy to chemical change — but rather, a very understandable desire on their part to investigate the claims of these chemical philosophers who suggested that the proper key to all nature was to be found in the study of this Christian, this Universal, and this experimental science — Chemistry.

MERTON REVISITED, or Science and Society in the Seventeenth Century

A. RUPERT HALL

A graduate of the University of Cambridge, A. Rupert Hall (1920—   ) is now Professor of the History of Science and Technology at Imperial College, London. He is the prolific author of articles and books on seventeenth-century English science, including: *Ballistics in the Seventeenth Century* (1952); *The Scientific Revolution: 1500—1800* (1954, 1962); and *From Galileo to Newton: 1630—1720* (1963). A co-editor of the Oxford *History of Technology* (1953—58), Hall is currently editing a projected eight-volume series covering developments in science from antiquity to the present time. With his wife, the historian of chemistry Marie Boas Hall, he has edited a selection of the *Unpublished Scientific Papers of Isaac Newton* (1962) and is preparing an edition of the correspondence of the Royal Society of London's first secretary, Henry Oldenburg.

A QUARTER OF A CENTURY AGO a brilliant young scholar . . . published a monograph with the title "Science, technology and society in seventeenth-century England." In this thorough, well-argued and closely written study Robert K. Merton presented with a wealth of documentary evidence the classical instance of the historical analysis of science as a social phenomenon. Merton conceived of science as a cultural artefact, a manifestation of intellectual energy that is stimulated, checked or modified by the structure, beliefs and aspirations of the society with which this scientific activity is associated. Put thus crudely the idea seems almost a truism; of course no one in writing the history of science would ever divorce it completely from society's beliefs and structure. Merton's monograph was far from being an exercise in the obvious, however, nor were the historiographical themes with which it was concerned trivial. It was Merton's contention that the historical study of a past society can provide principles of historical explanation which are complementary to, if they do not replace, those offered by the historian of science. Particularly, sociological history provides (if I follow Merton's view of 1938 correctly) principles sufficing to explain that crucial event, the scientific revolution of the seventeenth century, even though the provision of such an explanation was not Merton's chief or explicit concern. In fact Merton may be said to have insisted that the major displacements in science do require sociological explanations.

Merton's challenge was not at once accepted and his study was greeted rather with the admiration it deserved than with argument or criticism. Looking back one can see why: Merton's work was the culmination of an established tradition, not the beginning of a new one. To say that it aroused no great astonishment does not detract from its importance, which lay in making a strong case for the sociological explanation in one country at one time. As Merton himself generously acknowledged, his thesis was not (in broad terms) singular to himself. But Merton could justly regard himself as offering clear ideas backed by

From A. Rupert Hall, "Merton Revisited, or Science and Society in the Seventeenth Century," *History of Science*, Vol. II (1963), pp. 1–15. Reprinted by permission of W. Heffer & Sons Ltd.

massive evidence, where his predecessors had brought forward little more than intuitions.

A current of historiography that favoured "externalist" explanations — ones deriving from the general cultural, economic and social state of a nation or community of nations — ran strongly in the nineteen twenties and thirties. It derived its ultimate strength from two majestic Victorian conceptions: Marx's observation that the character of a society is largely determined by its economy, together with the compatible though distinct discovery of the anthropologists that "culture" is a unity. Adding these two ideas together, one is led to conclude that a man's thoughts on any one topic — say, celestial mechanics — are not independent of his thoughts on all other topics, nor of the economic state of the society in which he lives. So far, if we allow that "not independent of" is by no means equivalent to "causally determined by," we have a historiographical notion that is, today, hardly open to dispute. Some thirty years ago, however, historians were more apt to regard the case as one of causal determinism and to suppose that any correlation between an intellectual event A and a social event B could be understood as justifying the view that B in some sense "caused" A, or at least was a necessary condition for the occurrence of A. Such interpretations of historical occurrences in the less fundamental realms of politics, religion and so on by reference to other phenomena in the more fundamental realms of economics seemed to promise escape from the general mistiness and subjectivism of historical explanation.

Social explanations in history appeared objective and certain because they avoid emphasis on individuality and the hazardous significance of the individual. Authoritative models were provided by (for example) Max Weber and R. H. Tawney, whose *Religion and the Rise of Capitalism* was published in 1926. Merton refers to the latter five times; remarking that "It is

misleading to assume that [the] foci of scientific interest are exclusively due to the intrinsic developments within the various sciences," he credits to Max Weber the observation that scientists commonly select for teatment problems which are vitally linked with the dominant values and interests of the day.

Quotations from the philosopher-historian A. N. Whitehead, the literary historian R. F. Jones, the economic historian G. N. Clark and such historians of science as Dorothy Stimson and Martha Ornstein add further support to Merton's point of view; even E. A. Burtt, who really belongs to a very different school of intellectual history, yields passages to the same effect. For his most uncompromising example of the "externalist" historiography of science, however, Merton turned to an essay "On the social and economic roots of Newton's *Principia*" by a Russian historian, B. Hessen, which is indeed a collector's piece.

There is no need now to go back beyond Merton's monograph. "Science, technology and society in seventeenth-century England" is both more complete and more sophisticated than any of its precursors. Merton saw the problem he proposed to himself as consisting of two parts: (1) why did "scientific development in England become especially marked about the middle of the seventeenth century?" and (2) "why was there a strong preponderance of interest, among those concerned, in the physical sciences?" That each part of the problem was real — that is, that the characteristic to be investigated was genuine — Merton established by quite elaborate statistical analyses, as well as by the independent testimony of historians of science.

To each part of the problem Merton devoted a distinct social explanation. In order to account for the increase of interest in science that took place in England, he argued that a distinct change in values associated with Puritanism favoured science; to account for the partiality of this interest towards physical science he instanced the problems of engineering, navigation, warfare and so forth that could be solved by means of physical science. . . .

SCIENCE AND TECHNOLOGY

Merton linked the two parts of his sociological study with these words:

if this congeniality of the Puritan and the scientific temper partly explains the increased tempo of scientific activity during the later seventeenth century, by no means does it account for the particular foci of scientific and technologic investigation. . . . Was the choice of problems a wholly personal concern, completely unrelated to the socio-cultural background? Or was this selection significantly limited and guided by social forces?

Once more, Merton made a statistical analysis — this time of Birch's *History of the Royal Society* — in order to display the character of scientific work; he assigned about 40 per cent of it to the category of "pure science" and the greater part of the rest to the fields of sea-transport, mining and military technology. After further strengthening his case by a review of the activities and attitudes of individual scientists, Merton concluded that the seventeenth-century English scientists' choice of problem was much influenced by socioeconomic considerations. Yet he was clearly far from supposing that science was *determined* by outside pressures, as Hessen had suggested, and lately he has made this point clearer still; for Merton technological considerations are not *all*, but neither are they *nothing*.

This opinion is unexceptionable. No one can deny that conceptual science, let alone experimental science, is shaped by the technological equipment of the time in some measure; but the interesting question is: how much and in what way? Is science (as it were) an unconscious as well as a conscious instrument of society, or is it not? To say merely, for example, that X was a scientist and X was also interested in practical problems of technology, is not really to tell us very much; the bare information certainly permits no inference about the relation between X's scientific and technological interests. If X is the Royal Society as depicted in Birch's *History*, Merton's analysis will tell us that many Fellows were more interested in craft problems than in scientific ones; that a Baconian view of the utility of science was commonplace; and that men had a naive view of the relationship between pure science and the mastery of nature. . . . But from such information, valuable and interesting as it is, we do not learn what seventeenth-century *science* was, nor does it serve to answer Merton's question: why were people more interested in physics than in biology? Nor does it answer Hessen's. Such inquiries tell us nothing about Boyle, or Hooke, or Newton, that is significant to consideration of their work as scientists. It is really of little benefit to an understanding of the scientific revolution from Galileo to Newton that quite a lot of men were interested in ships, cabbages, and sealing-wax.

As with the religious issue, the matter must be clearly and definitely put if it is to have significance. When and in what circumstances is one entitled to infer that a particular piece of scientific work was done for some extra-scientific reason? Those who maintain that often or in some telling way this is the case should lay down their principles of inference. To consider a recent example: by 1940 many physicists knew that the release of nuclear energy was possible, and many worked on the problem during subsequent years. Does this mean — by inference — that all physicists working in atomic physics before 1940 did so because they believed that their work would lead to the technological use of nuclear energy? Of course not. What is the difference when Newton wrote in the scholium to Proposition XXXIV of Book II of the *Principia*: "This proposition I conceive may be of use in the building of ships"? Was Newton's interest in physics conditioned by the needs (in applied hydrodynamics) of the society in which he lived? It is trivially obvious that Newton could not have written these words if he had been unaware of things called ships, and indeed could not have written the *Principia* at all if he had not been aware of moving bodies, pendulums and so forth. It is perhaps a little more interesting that a mathematician should think such a remark worth making at a time when no master-shipwright employed a mathematical theory or would have admitted the competence of a mathematical physicist to instruct him. Yet this statement of Newton's is quoted in a portion of Merton's monograph from which the conclusion is drawn:

In general, then, it may be said that the contemporary scientists, ranging from the indefatigable virtuoso Petty to the nonpareil Newton, definitely focused their attention upon technical tasks made prominent by problems of navigation and upon derivative scientific research.

To me, this makes Newton sound like a superior carpenter, cartographer, or compass-maker; it puts him in the class of such excellent and learned practitioners as Captain Samuel Sturmy or Joseph Moxon. An analysis that confuses mathematical physics with mathematical technology in this way bewilders rather than assists the historian of science. . . .

In its crudest forms at any rate the socioeconomic interpretation of the scientific revolution as an offshoot of rising capitalism and mercantile militarism has perished without comment. Its unilluminating conclusions rested on defective logic and improbable psychology; very often, as I myself have tried to reveal, the true situation is far too complicated to yield such simple generalisations as "mathematicians were inspired to seek solutions to gunners' problems." In fact the influence of the art of war on seventeenth-century physics was negligible though (remembering Merton's words) we must not say there was *no* such influence. Hence some of the strongest reasons for the decline of the economic hypothesis are

well expressed in the words of one of the most distinguished of modern economic historians, John W. Nef:

If we examine the background of the intellectual revolution that is responsible for the industrial world in which we live today, we find little to support the view that modern science resulted from industrial progress in the north of Europe between the Reformation and the (English) Civil War. During these times of decisive change in rational procedures it was the mind itself, not economic institutions nor economic development, which called the new tunes and composed most of the variations which the greatest scientists were playing on them. The revolutionary scientific discoveries by Gilbert, Harvey, Galileo and Kepler, like the new mathematics of Descartes, Desargues, Fermat and Pascal, were of no immediate practical use. Freedom, rather than necessity, was the principal power behind the scientific revolution.

Thus recent historians reverse the arrow of economic inference: social forms do not dominate mind; rather, in the long run, mind determines social forms.

THE ASCENDANCY OF THE INTELLECT

In 1939, one year after Merton's monograph, there appeared the *Études galiléennes* of Alexandre Koyré. No contributions to the history of science could be less alike. It is beside my purpose to develop the contrast, save by the obvious remark that as Merton summed up one epoch, that of the socioeconomic historian Koyré opened another, that of the intellectual historian. Of course Koyré was no more first in the field than Merton was; in their different ways Tannery, Duhem, Cassirer, Mach, Meyerson and Lovejoy had initiated the history of ideas long before. None of Koyré's predecessors, however, had begun that analysis of the scientific revolution as a phenomenon of intellectual history which Koyré has made peculiarly his own. Among the younger historians of science especially his has been the dominant influence through the last ten or fifteen years, and this influence has had a marked effect in withdrawing interest from externalist explanations; other factors have of course worked in the same direction.

Such externalist forms of historical explanation as the sociological tend to confine the intellectual development of science within rather narrow bounds; it is a fundamental hypothesis of this historiography that the gross character of the science of any epoch is shaped externally, the intellectual or internal structure of science affecting only the minutiae and technicalities. To summarise Merton's view, for instance:

short-time fluctuations of interest in mathematics are largely explicable in terms of the appearance of important contributions by individual mathematicians . . . the foci of interest within the general field are partially determined by the nature of the problems which have been explained or brought to light. [Further, the] conclusion that the minor, short-time fluctuations in scientific interest are primarily determined by the internal history of the science in question is borne out by other facts. [The influence of Gilbert and Harvey is discussed.] In a sense, then, the study of these short-time fluctuations would seem the province of the historian of science rather than that of the sociologist or student of culture.

Here, it is clear the "long-time" fluctuations are not assigned to the province of the historian of science. Such a view is consistent with a "ripeness of time" concept of discovery or originality: we cannot (according to this concept) attach any special significance to the work of Newton in 1687, Darwin in 1859, or Einstein in 1905 because the time was ripe on each occasion for the work and if Newton, Darwin or Einstein had not written as they did some one else (Hooke, Wallace) would have served the same function. Only in a shorthand way therefore did Newton and the others have a permanent influence on science. Merton did not teach this view, but he did write that

specific discoveries and inventions belong to the internal history of science and are largely independent of factors other than the purely scientific.

A true, but a curiously negative statement. Why should not the general development of (say) astronomy in the seventeenth century be "largely independent of factors other than the purely scientific" and not merely the discovery of a fifth satellite of Saturn? This latter opinion has indeed been adopted by those who have followed Koyré in opposing the endeavour to credit the strategy of the scientific revolution to nonscientific influences. In the *Études* Koyré himself renounced just that liaison between modern physical science and empiricism which was regarded as crucial in the early nineteen-thirties; he has rejected also the thesis that classical science is "active" in the way postulated by the Protestant historians. For Koyré and many others since — as earlier for Burtt — the scientific revolution is to be understood as a transformation of intellectual attitudes:

Aussi croyons-nous, que l'attitude intellectuelle de la science classique pourrait être caractérisée par ces deux moments, étroitement liés d'ailleurs: géométrisation de l'espace, et dissolution du Cosmos . . . cette attitude intellectuelle nous paraît avoir été le fruit d'une mutation décisive. . . . C'est qu'il s'agissait non pas de combattre des théories erronées, ou insuffisantes, mais de *transformer les cadres de l'intelligence elle-même.* . . .

There is no suggestion here that the new intellectual attitude was generated by or dependent upon anything external to science, nor does Koyré ever contemplate such a thing. The intellectual change is one whose explanation must be sought in the history of the intellect; to this extent (and we need not pause now to expound all the obvious provisos about microscopes, X-rays, cyclotrons and so forth) the history of science is strictly analogous to the history of philosophy. It is no accident that Koyré himself is a philosopher, nor that an English philosopher-historian should have expressed in *The idea of Nature* a vision of the scientific revolution similar to his. When Collingwood wrote

the Renaissance philosophers enrolled themselves under the banner of Plato against the Aristotelians, until Galileo, the true father of modern science, restated the Pythagorean-Platonic standpoint in his own words by proclaiming that the book of nature is a book written by God in the language of mathematics

he asserted, as Koyré has asserted, that modern science is of its own intellectual right fundamental and absolute; it is not derivative from some other displacement in civilization such as the reformation or the rise of capitalism. The historians of religion have never claimed that the reformation "transformed the very structure of the intellect" and it would be indeed odd if someone holding this view of the transcendent significance of the scientific revolution should also consider it as a mere epiphenomenon. One who has written on the history of religion, Herbert Butterfield, put it no less strongly ten years later, declaring that the scientific revolution "outshines everything since the rise of Christianity and reduces the Renaissance and Reformation to the rank of mere episodes, mere internal displacements, within the system of medieval Christendom."

If modern science is the fruit of an intellectual mutation its genesis must be considered in relation to an intellectual tradition; to quote Butterfield once more, its sources stretch far "back in an unmistakably continuous line to a period much earlier" than the sixteenth century. Those who find the origins of science in the Puritan-capitalist complex, however, have no need for and see little value in the evidence for continuity in scientific thought. On the whole they have been empiricists rather than rationalists. Despite the scholarly researches of Duhem, Sudhoff, Little and many others, the Middle Ages did not get a good press from historians of science during the first two decades of this century; only after Sarton, Haskins, Thorndike and

their generation had filled in many more details and suggested new interpretations did Duhem's thesis command widespread attention. Even in 1948 Jean Pelseneer wrote of Duhem:

Nul plus que lui n'a donné, quand on le lit, l'impression d'une continuité si complète dans l'histoire de la science, que l'on finit par douter d'un progrès véritable; chaque auteur paraît n'avoir fait que soubir les connaissances de ses prédécesseurs. . . . L'influence reçue étant en raison inverse du mérite, de l'originalité, il en résulte l'impossibilité de planifier avec succès la recherche scientifique.

That is, the very measure of the genius which could give birth to modern science is the fact that its departure from past traditions was so great, and effected so complete a breach of continuity. Merton, who made no reference to either Duhem or Wohlwill, saw a parallel lack of continuity in the attitudes of society to science. He contrasted Richard Baxter's view of science with that of the Middle Ages as he saw it:

To regard with high esteem scientific discoveries attained empirically and without reference to Scriptural or other sacred authority would have been almost as heretical as making the discoveries themselves. As Professor Haskins has observed, the scientific spirit of Christian Europe in the Middle Ages was not liberated from the respect for authority which was characteristic of that epoch, whereas Puritan authority was enunciating the very doctrines which furthered interest in science and, ultimately, lack of concern with religion itself.

Neither Pelseneer's criticism nor Merton's comparison is wholly unjust. Nevertheless most historians would nowadays emphasise the discontinuity between medieval and modern science much less strongly and in very different terms. Certainly dissent from Duhem's thesis does exist — that thesis has been firmly criticised by Anneliese Maier for instance — and some of the most effective of the intellectual historians, Koyré among them, are far from regarding the scientific revolution as fully prepared in the

Middle Ages. Meanwhile, different forms of the case for continuity in dynamics, kinematics, optics, epistemology and so on have been prepared by Marshall Clagett, A. C. Crombie, E. A. Moody and J. H. Randall; even if their work is not considered conclusive in every respect it is far from being negligible. In fact the intellectual historians are by no means divided among themselves on the issue of continuity in the way that they, as a group, are divided from the socio-economic historians. All are agreed, for example, that early modern science was in some measure indebted to medieval science; and that if seventeenth century concepts are not identical with those of the fourteenth there is an intellectual connection between them.

Even without making a detailed review of the work of other historians of science active at the present time it is clear that the trend towards intellectual history is strong and universal. Since the journal *Centaurus* published in 1953 a special group of articles on the social relations of science no single article that can be judged to represent the sociological interpretation of history has appeared in that periodical, or *Isis, Annals of science, Revue d'histoire des sciences* or the *Archives internationales*. There has been little discussion of the historiographical issue: indeed, it sometimes seems that the case for setting the development of scientific thought in its broader historical context is condemned before it is heard, though one knows from personal conversations that this is not neglected in pedagogic practice. Clearly, externalist explanations of the history of science have lost their interest as well as their interpretative capacity. One reason for this may be that such explanations tell us very little about science itself; about the reception of Newton's optical discoveries, or the significance of Galileo's ideas in mechanics, or about concepts of combustion and animal heat. Social and economic relations are rather concerned with the scientific movement than with science as a system of knowledge of nature (theoretical and prac-

tical); they help us to understand the public face of science and the public reaction to scientists; to evaluate the propaganda that scientists distribute about themselves, and occasionally — but only occasionally — to see why the subject of scientific discussion takes a new turn. But to understand the true contemporary significance of some piece of work in science, to explore its antecedents and effects, in other words to recreate critically the true historical situation, for this we must treat science as intellectual history, even experimental science. A sociologist like Merton understood this, of course; what he doubted was the significance of such intellectual history divorced from the social context which was, naturally, his main focus of interest.

Profoundly different historical points of view are involved. It is not enough to suggest, as Lilley modestly did, that there is a bit of truth in both of them so that

the development of science can be fully understood only if the internal and external types of influence are considered together and in their mutual interaction.

(The suggestion that the very stuff of science, that which it *is* at any moment, should ever be considered as an internal *influence,* is rather curious.) To suppose that it is not worth while to take sides or that the determination of the historian's own attitude to the issue is not significant is to jeopardise the existence of the historiography of science as more than narration and chronicle. For example: how is the historian to conceive of science, before he undertakes to trace its development; is he to conceive it as above all a deep intellectual enterprise whose object it is to gain some comprehension of the cosmos in terms which are, in the last resort, philosophical? Or as an instruction-book for a bag of tricks by which men master natural resources and each other? Is a scientific theory a partial, temporally-limited vision of nature or a useful message printed on a little white card that pops out of a machine when the social animal presses the button — different cards for different buttons, of course? I have deliberately given an exaggerated emphasis to these rhetorical questions in order to indicate the violent imbalance between two points of view that one simply cannot ignore nor amalgamate. In the same way the historian's concept of the scientific revolution of the seventeenth century is historiographically dependent. One issue between the externalist and the internalist interpretation is this: was the beginning of modern science the outstanding feature of early modern civilisation, or must it yield in importance to others, such as the Reformation or the development of capitalism? Before 1940 most general historians and many historians of science would have adopted the latter position; since 1940 nearly all historians have adopted the former one. Why this change should have come about it is not hard to imagine.

By this I do not mean to suggest that the problems raised by the sociologists of science are obsolete; on the contrary, as some scientists like J. D. Bernal have been saying for a long time and many more are saying now, they are immensely real and direct at this moment. Consequently the historical evolution of this situation is of historical significance too, and I believe we shall return to its consideration when a certain revulsion from the treatment of scientists as puppets has been overcome, when (if ever) we are less guiltily involved in the situation ourselves so that we can review it without passion, and when a fresh approach has been worked out. This will not, I imagine, take the form so much of a fusion between two opposite positions in the manner of the Hegelian dialectic, as the demarcation of their respective fields of application with some degree of accuracy. There may also develop a socio-techno-economic historiography whose study will be the gradual transformation of society by science and not (as too often in the past) the rapid transformation of science by society. All this will require a fine analysis, a scrupulous drawing of distinctions and a careful avoidance (except under strict controls) of evidence drawn from subjective, propagandist and programmatic sources. A true sociology of science will deal with what actually happened and could happen, not with what men thought might happen or should happen.

THE SIGNIFICANCE OF THE
NEWTONIAN SYNTHESIS

ALEXANDRE KOYRÉ

A search for the founders of the study of the history of science could lead
one to some eighteenth-century figures—Joseph Priestley, J. B. J. Delambre—
but it would more likely include scholars of the late nineteenth and early twentieth centuries whose influence is still with us—Pierre Duhem, Paul Tannery,
George Sarton, Lynn Thorndike. These are the men who helped establish the
history of science as a scholarly discipline. If one were to seek, on the other
hand, the source of the modern internalist interpretation of the growth of science,
the search would center on one man: Alexandre Koyré (1892–1964). It is true
that he was not the first to point out the need to study scientific concepts within
their historical setting, instead of rating them in terms of their place in the
twentieth century scheme of science. Nor was he the first to emphasize the
intellectual, the philosophical, the metaphysical roots of science. Nevertheless,
through example—his definitive monographs on Galileo and Newton—and
exhortation he directed the modern generation of historians of science to pay
less attention to the fact-gathering and instrumentation side of science and to
concern themselves with the more fundamental, and fruitful, problems associated
with the conceptual analysis of science.

Born in Taganrog, Russia, Koyré studied philosophy, physics, and mathematics at the University of Göttingen, the Ecole Pratique des Hautes Études,
and the Collège de France. At his death in 1964 he was Directeur d'Études à
l'École Pratique des Hautes Études and a member of the Princeton Institute for
Advanced Study.

ALL OF US, or if not all, still most of us, have been born and bred — or better and more exactly, not *born* (as this is impossible) but only *bred* — in the Newtonian or, at least, a semi-Newtonian world, and we have all, or neary all, accepted the
idea of the Newtonian world machine as the expression of the true picture of the
universe and the embodiment of scientific truth — this because for more than two hundred years such has been the common creed, the *communis opinio*, of modern science and of enlightened mankind.

Thus it seems to me that I have the right to assume that when we are speaking about
Newton and Newtonianism we know more or less what we are speaking of. More or
less! Somehow this very expression used in connection with Newton strikes me as improper, because it is possible that the deep-est meaning and aim of Newtonianism, or
rather, of the whole scientific revolution of the seventeenth century, of which Newton
is the heir and the highest expression, is just to abolish the world of the "more or
less," the world of qualities and sense per-ception, the world of appreciation of our
daily life, and to replace it by the (Archi-medean) universe of precision, of exact
measures, of strict determination.

Let us dwell for a moment upon this revolution, one of the deepest, if not the

From "The Significance of the Newtonian Synthesis," Alexandre Koyré, *Newtonian Studies*. Harvard
University Press (Cambridge, Mass., 1965), pp. 3–24. Reprinted with permission of Madame Alexandre Koyré.

deepest, mutations and transformations accomplished — or suffered — by the human mind since the invention of the cosmos by the Greeks, two thousand years before. This revolution has been described and explained — much more explained than described — in quite a number of ways. Some people stress the role of experience and experiment in the new science, the fight against bookish learning, the new belief of modern man in himself, in his ability to discover truth by his own powers, by exercising his senses and his intelligence, so forcefully expressed by Bacon and by Descartes, in contradistinction to the formerly prevailing belief in the supreme and overwhelming value of tradition and consecrated authority.

Some others stress the practical attitude of modern man, who turns away from the *vita contemplativa,* in which the medieval and antique mind allegedly saw the very acme of human life, to the *vita activa;* who therefore is no longer able to content himself with pure speculation and theory; and who wants a knowledge that can be put to use: a *scientia activa, operativa,* as Bacon called it, or, as Descartes has said, a science that would make man master and possessor of nature.

The new science, we are told sometimes, is the science of the craftsman and the engineer, of the working, enterprising, and calculating tradesman, in fact, the science of the rising bourgeois classes of modern society.

There is certainly some truth in these descriptions and explanations: it is clear that the growth of modern science presupposes that of the cities, it is obvious that the development of firearms, especially of artillery, drew attention to problems of ballistics; that navigation, especially that to America and India, furthered the building of clocks, and so forth — yet I must confess that I am not satisfied with them. I do not see what the *scientia activa* has ever had to do with the development of the calculus, nor the rise of the bourgeoisie with that of the Copernican, or the Keplerian, astron-

omy. And as for experience and experiment — two things which we must not only distinguish but even oppose to each other — I am convinced that the rise and growth of experimental science is not the source but, on the contrary, the result of the new *theoretical,* that is, the new *metaphysical* approach to nature that forms the content of the scientific revolution of the seventeenth century, a content which we have to understand before we can attempt an explanation (whatever this may be) of its historical occurrence.

I shall therefore characterize this revolution by two closely connected and even complementary features: (*a*) the destruction of the cosmos, and therefore the disappearance from science — at least in principle, if not always in fact — of all considerations based on this concept, and (*b*) the geometrization of space, that is, the substitution of the homogeneous and abstract — however now considered as real — dimension space of the Euclidean geometry for the concrete and differentiated place-continuum of pre-Galilean physics and astronomy.

As a matter of fact, this characterization is very nearly equivalent to the mathematization (geometrization) of nature and therefore the mathematization (geometrization) of science.

The disappearance — or destruction — of the cosmos means that the world of science, the real world, is no more seen, or conceived, as a finite and hierarchically ordered, therefore qualitatively and ontologically differentiated, whole, but as an open, indefinite, and even infinite universe, united not by its immanent structure but only by the identity of its fundamental contents and laws; a universe in which, in contradistinction to the traditional conception with its separation and opposition of the two worlds of becoming and being, that is, of the heavens and the earth, all its components appear as placed on the same ontological level; a universe in which the *physica coelestis* and *physica terrestris* are identified and unified, in which astronomy and physics become interdependent and united because of their common subjection to geometry.

This, in turn, implies the disappearance — or the violent expulsion — from scientific thought of all considerations based on value, perfection, harmony, meaning, and aim, because these concepts, from now on *merely subjective,* cannot have a place in the new ontology. Or, to put it in different words: all formal and final causes as modes of explanation disappear from — or are rejected by — the new science and are replaced by efficient and even material ones. Only these latter have right of way and are admitted to existence in the new universe of hypostatized geometry and it is only in this abstract-real (Archimedean) world, where abstract bodies move in an abstract space, that the laws of being and of motion of the new — the classical — science are valid and true.

It is easy now to understand why classical science — as has been said so often — has substituted a world of quantity for that of quality: just because, as Aristotle already knew quite well, there are no qualities in the world of numbers, or in that of geometrical figures. There is no place for them in the realm of mathematical ontology.

And even more. It is easy now to understand why classical science — as has been seen so seldom — has substituted a world of being for the world of becoming and change: just because, as Aristotle has said too, there is no change and no becoming in numbers and in figures. But, in doing so, it was obliged to reframe and to reformulate or rediscover its fundamental concepts, such as those of matter, motion, and so on.

If we take into account the tremendous scope and bearing of this so deep and so radical revolution, we shall have to admit that, on the whole, it has been surprisingly quick.

It was in 1543 — one hundred years before the birth of Newton — that Copernicus wrested the earth from its foundations and hurled it into the skies. It was in the beginning of the century (1609 and 1619) that Kepler formulated his laws of celestial mo-

tions and thus destroyed the orbs and spheres that encompassed the world and held it together; and did it at the same time that Galileo, creating the first scientific instruments and showing to mankind things that no human eye had ever seen before, opened to scientific investigation the two connected worlds of the infinitely great and the infinitely small.

Moreover, it was by his "subjecting motion to number" that Galileo cleared the way for the formulation of the new concepts of matter and motion I have just mentioned, which formed the basis of the new science and cosmology; concepts with the aid of which— identifying matter and space — Descartes, in 1637, tried, and failed, to reconstruct the world; concepts that — redistinguishing between matter and space — Newton so brilliantly, and so successfully, used in his own reconstruction.

The new concept of motion which so victoriously asserts itself in the classical science is quite a simple one, so simple that, although very easy to use — once one is accustomed to it, as we all are — it is very difficult to grasp and fully to understand. Even for us, I cannot analyze it here, yet I would like to point out that, as Descartes quite clearly tells us, it substitutes a purely mathematical notion for a physical one and that, in opposition to the pre-Galilean and pre-Cartesian conception, which understood motion as a species of becoming, as a kind of process of change that affected the bodies subjected to it, in contradistinction to rest, which did not, the new — or classical — conception interprets motion as a kind of being, that is, not as a process, but as a *status,* a *status* that is just as permanent and indestructible as rest and that no more than this latter affects the bodies that are in motion. . . .

The motion dealt with in this law is not the motion of the bodies of our experience; we do not encounter it in our daily lives. It is the motion of geometrical (Archimedean) bodies in abstract space. That is the reason why it has nothing to do with change. The "motion" of geometrical bodies in geometrical space changes nothing at all; the "places" in such a space are equivalent and even identical. It is a changeless change, if I may say so, a strange and paradoxical blending together of the same and the other that Plato tried — and failed — to effect in his *Parmenides*.

The transformation of the concept of motion by substituting for the empirical concept the hypostatized mathematical one is inevitable if we have to subject motion to number in order to deal with it mathematically, to build up a mathematical physics. But this is not enough. Conversely, mathematics itself has to be transformed (and to have achieved this transformation is the undying merit of Newton). Mathematical entities have to be, in some sense, brought nearer to physics, subjected to motion, and viewed not in their "being" but in their "becoming" or in their "flux."

The curves and figures of geometry have to be seen, and understood, not as built up of other geometrical elements, not as cut out in space by the intersection of geometrical bodies and planes, nor even as presenting a spatial image of the structural relations expressed in themselves by algebraic formulas, but as engendered or described by the motion of points and lines in space. It is a timeless motion, of course, that we are here dealing with, or, even stranger, a motion in a timeless time — a notion as paradoxical as that of changeless change. Yet it is only by making a changeless change proceed in timeless time that we can deal — effectively as well as intellectually — with such realities as speed, acceleration, or direction of a moving body in any point of its trajectory, or, *vice versa*, at any moment of the motion describing that trajectory. . . .

The physicomathematical current I have just been sketching is certainly the most original and most important trend of seventeenth-century scientific thought. Yet, parallel to it there runs another one, less mathematical, less deductive, more empirical and experimental. Being less pretentious (or more diffident), it does not attempt the sweeping generalizations of the mathematicians. It views them with misgiving and even with hostility and it restricts itself to the discovery of new facts and to the building up of partial theories explaining them.

This current is inspired not by the Platonic idea of the mathematical structure and determination of being, but by the Lucretian, Epicurean, Democritean conception of its atomic composition (strange as it may seem, most modern ideas lead back to some old Greek fancy). Gassendi, Roberval, Boyle (the best representative of their groups), Hooke — they all oppose the more timid, more cautious, and more secure *corpuscular philosophy* to the panmathematism of Galileo and Descartes.

Thus when Galileo tells us that the book of nature — that book in which the medieval mind perceived the *vestigia* and the *imagines Dei* and read the glory of God expressed in sensible symbols of beauty and splendor revealing the hidden meaning and aim of the creation — was, in truth, written in geometrical characters, in circles, triangles, and squares, and only told us the intellectually marvelous story of rational connection and order, Boyle protests: the book of nature, said he, was certainly "a well-contrived romance" of which every part, "written in the stenography of God's omniscient hand," stood in relation to every other; but it was written not in geometrical but in *corpuscular* characters.

Not mathematical structure but corpuscular texture formed for him the inner reality of being. In the explanation of the universe we have to start with — or stop at — matter, not homogeneous Cartesian matter, but matter already formed by God into various, diversely determined corpuscles. These are the letters which motion forms into the words of the divine romance.

Looking at things from this perspective we see quite clearly that Newton presents us with a synthesis of both trends, of both views. For him, just as for Boyle, the book of nature is written in corpuscular characters and words. But, just as for Galileo and

Descartes, it is a purely mathematical syntax that binds them together and gives its meaning to the text of the book.

Thus, in contradistinction to the world of Descartes, the world of Newton is conceived as composed not of two (extension and motion) but of three elements: (1) *matter*, that is, an infinite number of mutually separated and isolated, hard and unchangeable — but not identical — particles; (2) *motion*, that strange and paradoxical relation-state that does not affect the particles in their being, but only transports them hither and thither in the infinite, homogeneous void; and (3) *space*, that is, this very infinite and homogeneous void in which, unopposed, the corpuscles (and the bodies built of them) perform their motions.

There is, of course, a fourth component in that Newtonian world, namely, attraction which binds and holds it together. Yet this is not an *element* of its construction; it is either a hyperphysical power — God's action — or a mathematical stricture that lays down the rule of syntax in God's book of nature.

The introduction of the void — with its correlative, attraction — into the world view of Newton, in spite of the tremendous physical and metaphysical difficulties involved by this conception (action at a distance; existence of the nothing), was a stroke of genius and a step of decisive importance. It is this step that enabled Newton to oppose and unite at the same time — and to do it *really*, and not *seemingly*, like Descartes — the discontinuity of matter and the continuity of space. The corpuscular structure of matter, emphatically asserted, formed a firm basis for the application of mathematical dynamics to nature. It yielded the *fundamenta* for the relations expressed by space. The cautious corpuscular philosophy did not really know what it was doing. But, as a matter of fact, it had been only showing the way to the Newtonian synthesis of mathematics and experiment.

The void . . . action through the void . . . action at a distance (attraction) — it was against these features and implications of the Newtonian world view that the opposition of the great Continental contemporaries of Newton — Huygens, Leibniz, Bernoulli — well trained in the Cartesian rejection of unclear and unintelligible ideas, was directed.

In his famous, brilliant *Lettres anglaises*, or, to give them their official title, *Lettres philosophiques* — readable even today — Voltaire very wittily sums up the situation: a Frenchman who arrives in London finds himself in a completely changed world. He left the world *full*; he finds it *empty*. In Paris the universe is composed of vortices of subtle matter; in London there is nothing of that kind. In Paris everything is explained by pressure which nobody understands; in London by attraction which nobody understands either.

Voltaire is perfectly right: the Newtonian world is chiefly composed of void. It is an infinite void, and only a very small part of it — an infinitesimal part — is filled up, or occupied, by matter, by bodies which, indifferent and unattached, move freely and perfectly unhampered in — and through — that boundless and bottomless abyss. And yet it is a world and not a chaotic congeries of isolated and mutually alien particles. This, because all of these are bound together by a very simple mathematical law of connection and integration — the law of attraction — according to which *every one of them is related to and united with every other*. Thus each one takes its part and plays its role in the building of the *systema mundi*.

The universal application of the law of attraction restores the physical unity of the Newtonian universe and, at the same time, gives it its intellectual unity. Identical relations hold together identical contents. In other words, it is the same set of laws which governs all the motions in the infinite universe: that of an apple which falls to the ground and that of the planets which move round the sun. Moreover, the very same laws explain not only the identical pattern (discovered by Kepler) of the celestial motions but even their individual differences, not only the regularities, but also the irregularities (inequalities). All the phenomena which for centuries baffled the sagacity of astronomers and physicists (such, for instance, as tides) appear as a result of the concatenation and combination of the same fundamental laws.

The Newtonian law of attraction according to which its force *diminishes* in proportion to the square of the distance is not only the only law of that kind that explains the facts but, besides, is the only one that can be uniformly and universally applied to large and small bodies, to apples and to the moon. It is the only one, therefore, that it was reasonable for God to have adopted as a law of creation.

Yet, in spite of all this, in spite of the rational plausibility and mathematical simplicity of the Newtonian law (the inverse-square law is simply the law of extension of spherical surfaces identical with that of the propagation of light), there was in it something that baffled the mind. Bodies attract each other, act upon each other (or, at least, behave as if they did). But how do they manage to perform this action, to overcome the chasm of the void that so radically separates and isolates them from each other? We must confess that nobody, not even Newton, could (or can) explain, or understand, this *how*.

Newton himself, as we well know, never admitted attraction as a "physical" force. Time and again he said, and repeated, that it was only a "mathematical force," that it was perfectly impossible — not only for matter but even for God — to act at a distance, that is, to exert action where the agent was not present; that the attractive force, therefore — and this gives us a singular insight into the limits of the so-called Newtonian empiricism — was not to be considered as one of the essential and fundamental properties of bodies (or matter), one of these properties such as extension, mobility, impenetrability, and mass, which could neither be diminished nor increased; that it was a property to be explained; that

he could not do it, and that, as he did not want to give a fanciful explanation when lacking a good theory, and as science (mathematical philosophy of nature) could perfectly well proceed without one, he preferred to give none (this is one meaning of his celebrated *Hypotheses non fingo*, and leave the question open. Yet, strange, or natural, as it may seem, nobody — with the single exception of Colin Maclaurin — followed him in that point. . . .

The overwhelming success of Newtonian physics made it practically inevitable that its particular features became thought of as essential for the building of science — of any kind of science — as such, and that all the new sciences that emerged in the eighteenth century — sciences of man and of society — tried to conform to the Newtonian pattern of empirico-deductive knowledge, and to abide by the rules laid down by Newton in his famous *Regulae philosophandi,* so often quoted and so often misunderstood. The results of this infatuation with Newtonian logic, that is, the results of the uncritical endeavor mechanically to apply Newtonian (or rather *pseudo* Newtonian) methods to fields quite different from that of their original application, have been by no means very happy, as we shall presently see. Yet, before turning our attention to these, in a certain sense illegitimate, offshoots of Newtonianism, we have to dwell for a moment upon the more general and more diffuse consequences of the universal adoption of the Newtonian synthesis, of which the most important seems to have been the tremendous reinforcement of the old dogmatic belief in the so-called "simplicity" of nature, and the reintroducing through science into this very nature of very important and very far-reaching elements of not only *factual* but even *structural* irrationality.

In other words, not only did Newton's physics use *de facto* such obscure ideas as power and attraction (ideas suggesting scholasticism and magic, protested the Continentals), not only did he give up the very idea of a rational deduction of the actual composition and formation of the choir of heaven and furniture of earth, but even its fundamental dynamic law (the inverse-square law), though plausible and reasonable, was by no means necessary, and, as Newton had carefully shown, could be quite different. Thus, the law of attraction itself was nothing more than a mere fact.

And yet the harmonious insertion of all these facts into the rational frame of spatio-mathematical order, the marvelous *compages* of the world, seemed clearly to exclude the subrationality of chance, but rather to imply the suprarationality of motive; it seemed perfectly clear that it had to be explained not by the necessity of cause, but by the freedom of choice.

The intricate and subtle machinery of the world seemed obviously to require a purposeful action, as Newton did not fail to assert. Or, to put it in Voltaire's words: the clockwork implies a clockmaker (*l'horloge implique l'horloger*).

Thus the Newtonian science, though as *mathematical philosophy of nature* it expressedly renounced the search for causes (both physical and metaphysical), appears in history as based on a dynamic conception of physical causality and as linked together with theistic or deistic metaphysics. This metaphysical system does not, of course, present itself as a constitutive or integrating part of the Newtonian science; it does not penetrate into its formal structure. Yet it is by no means an accident that not only for Newton himself, but also for all the Newtonians — with the exception only of Laplace — this science implied a reasonable belief in God.

Once more the book of nature seemed to reveal God, an engineering God this time, who not only had made the world clock, but who continuously had to supervise and tend it in order to mend its mechanism when needed (a rather bad clockmaker, this Newtonian God, objected Leibniz), thus manifesting his active presence and interest in his creation. . . .

The enthusiastic imitation (or pseudo-imitation) of the Newtonian (or pseudo-Newtonian) pattern of atomic analysis and reconstruction that up to our times proved to be so successful in physics, in chemistry, and even in biology, led elsewhere to rather bad results. Thus the unholy alliance of Newton and Locke produced an atomic psychology, which explained (or explained away) mind as a mosaic of "sensations" and "ideas" linked together by laws of association (attraction); we have had, too, atomic sociology, which reduced society to a cluster of human atoms, complete and self-contained each in itself and only mutually attracting and repelling each other.

Newton, of course, is by no means responsible for these, and other, *monstra* engendered by the overextension — or aping — of his method. Nor is he responsible for the more general, and not less disastrous, consequence of the widespread adoption of the atomic pattern of analysis of global events and actions according to which these latter appeared to be not *real,* but only *mathematical* results and summings up of the underlying elementary factors. This type of analysis led to the nominalistic misconception of the relation between a *totum* and its parts, a misconception which, as a matter of fact, amounted to a complete negation of *tota* (a *totum* reduced to a mere sum of its parts is not a *totum*) and which nineteenth- and twentieth-century thought has had such difficulty in overcoming. No man can ever be made responsible for the misuse of his work or the misinterpretation of his thought, even if such a misuse or misinterpretation appears to be — or to have been — historically inevitable.

Yet there is something for which Newton — or better to say not Newton alone, but modern science in general — can still be made responsible: it is the splitting of our world in two. I have been saying that modern science broke down the barriers that separated the heavens and the earth, and that it united and unified the universe. And that is true. But, as I have said, too, it did this by substituting for our world of quality and sense perception, the world in which we live, and love, and die, another world — the world of quantity, or reified geometry, a world in which, though there is place for everything, there is no place for man. Thus the world of science — the real world — became estranged and utterly divorced from the world of life, which science has been unable to explain — not even to explain away by calling it "subjective."

True, these worlds are every day — and even more and more — connected by the *praxis*. Yet for *theory* they are divided by an abyss.

Two worlds: this means two truths. Or no truth at all.

This is the tragedy of modern mind which "solved the riddle of the universe," but only to replace it by another riddle: the riddle of itself.

SUGGESTIONS FOR ADDITIONAL READING

Any research on the rise of modern science must begin with a reading of the original works which have been condensed here. By condensing the authors' statements, the editor is able to present the essential features of the various interpretations but he is unable to reproduce the full scholarly apparatus — footnotes, graphs, charts, appendices, etc. — used by many of the authors in support of their positions. This is especially true of the Merton selection, where a 275-page monograph has been drastically abridged and shorn of the sociologist's careful documentation.

Because most history students are not acquainted with the historical facts associated with the development of science in the sixteenth and seventeenth centuries, they should turn to one of the recent histories of science covering that period. Herbert Butterfield, *The Origins of Modern Science: 1300–1800* (New York, 1957), is the best short introduction to the subject. After Butterfield, in order of increasing comprehensiveness and complexity, one may read: A. Rupert Hall, *The Scientific Revolution: 1500–1800* (London, 1962); Marie Boas, *The Scientific Renaissance: 1450–1630* (New York, 1962); A. Rupert Hall, *From Galileo to Newton: 1630–1720* (New York, 1963); René Taton, ed., *The Beginnings of Modern Science: From 1450–1800* (New York, 1964); E. J. Dijksterhuis, *The Mechanization of the World Picture* (Oxford, 1961). A historian of philosophy, John Herman Randall, Jr., has published a volume correlating the philosophical and scientific ideas and movements predominant in this era: *The Career of Philosophy: From the Middle Ages to the Enlightenment* (New York, 1962).

Historians have not systematically gathered and studied the scattered remarks made by the early scientists on the origins of their discipline. A beginning has been made by Herbert Weisinger in his article "The Idea of the Renaissance and the Rise of Science," *Lychnos* (1946–47) and by A. C. Crombie in "Historians and the Scientific Revolution," *Endeavour*, XIX, no. 73 (1960). Lynn Thorndike, "Newness and Craving for Novelty in Seventeenth-Century Science and Medicine," *Journal of the History of Ideas*, XIII, no. 4 (1951), recorded over one hundred seventeenth-century books whose title or contents revealed the contemporary awareness of the recent appearance of science, but he did not discuss the full implications of his listings.

The eighteenth- and nineteenth-century defenders of the traditional interpretation of the emergence of modern science have not received any special attention from historians. Once again, Herbert Weisinger has made a preliminary study — "English Treatment of the Relationship Between the Rise of Science and the Renaissance, 1740–1840," *Annals of Science*, VII, no. 3 (1951) — and there is available a good general appraisal of William Whewell: Walter F. Cannon, "William Whewell, F.R.S., Contributions to Science and Learning," *Notes and Records of the Royal Society of London*, XIX, no. 2 (1964). Jakob Burckhardt, of course, has fared better, and material supplementing Baron's and Rosen's defense will be listed in a subsequent paragraph.

A. C. Crombie's *Medieval and Early Modern Science*, 2 vols. (New York, 1959) is the best interpretative and bibliographical guide to the scientific thought of the Middle Ages. Also pertinent are his articles: "The Relevance of the Middle Ages to the Scientific Movement," *Perspectives in Medieval History*, ed. K. F. Drew and F. S. Lear (Chicago, 1963); and "The Significance of Medieval Discussions of Scientific Method for the Scientific Revolution," *Critical Problems in the History of Science*, ed. M. Clagett (Madison, 1959). For any serious study one must refer to the pioneering researches of Pierre Duhem: *Les Origines de la Statique*, 2 vols. (Paris, 1905–06); *Études sur Léonard de Vinci*, 3 vols.

(Paris, 1906–13); and *Le Système du monde: Histoire des doctrines cosmologiques de Platon à Copernic,* 10 vols. (Paris, 1913–59). And then there are the scholars who have extended and revised Duhem's original contributions: Marshall Clagett, *The Science of Mechanics in the Middle Ages* (Madison, 1959); A. C. Crombie, *Robert Grosseteste and the Origins of Experimental Science* (Oxford, 1953); Charles H. Haskins, *Studies in the History of Medieval Science* (Cambridge, Mass., 1927); Anneliese Maier, *Die Vorläufer Galileis im 14. Jahrhundert* (Rome, 1949); Anneliese Maier, *Zwei Grundprobleme der scholastischen Naturphilosophie* (Rome, 1951); *Zwischen Philosophie und Mechanik* (Rome, 1958); and Lynn Thorndike, *A History of Magic and Experimental Science,* 8 vols. (New York, 1923–58). Finally, four shorter studies are recognized as classic statements on the medieval origins of modern science: Dana B. Durand, "Nicole Oresme and the Medieval Origins of Modern Science," *Speculum,* XVI, no. 2 (1941); Dana B. Durand, "Tradition and Innovation in Fifteenth Century Italy," *Journal of the History of Ideas,* IV, no. 1 (1943); John Herman Randall, Jr., "The Development of Scientific Method in the School of Padua," *Journal of the History of Ideas,* I, no. 2 (1940); Lynn White, Jr., "Natural Science and Naturalistic Art in the Middle Ages," *American Historical Review,* LII, no. 3 (1947).

Renaissance science is necessarily involved with the more general problem of the Renaissance. There are two excellent surveys of the historical literature generated by this problem. One of the surveys is itself a superb piece of scholarship — Wallace K. Ferguson, *The Renaissance in Historical Thought; Five Centuries of Interpretation* (Boston, 1948); the other is much shorter and is specifically written for the history student — Karl H. Dannenfeldt, *The Renaissance: Medieval or Modern?* (Boston 1959). Three significant appraisals of Renaissance science were produced by the distinguished historian of science George

Sarton shortly before his death in 1956. The first was addressed to a popular audience in 1952: "The Quest for Truth: Scientific Progress During the Renaissance" in *The Renaissance: A Symposium* (New York, 1953). The second stresses bibliographical information on the older sources of Renaissance science: *The Appreciation of Ancient and Medieval Science During the Renaissance* (Philadelphia, 1955). The final one makes extensive use of biographical data: *Six Wings: Men of Science in the Renaissance* (Bloomington, 1957). Sarton's assessment should be supplemented by W. P. D. Wightman's thematic analysis to be found in his: *Science and the Renaissance: An Introduction to the Study of the Emergence of the Sciences in the Sixteenth Century.* I (Aberdeen, 1962).

That the socioeconomic interpretation need not be based on Marxist ideology is clearly evident from Herbert Weisinger's study of the pre-Maxist sources of this viewpoint: "The English Origins of the Sociological Interpretation of the Renaissance," *Journal of the History of Ideas,* XI, no. 3 (1950). For an earlier example of this approach see Muhsin Mahdi, *Ibn Khaldûn's Philosophy of History* (Chicago, 1957), chap. IV.

Despite these precursors, the Marxist philosophy of history was largely responsible for a renewed interest in the social and economic roots of modern science. Neal Wood, in Chapter V of his *Communism and British Intellectuals* (New York, 1959), discusses the impact of Bukharin and Hessen on British scientists and journalists. One of these scientists, J. D. Bernal, has written a book which, in part, discusses the Marxist position on science and society — *The Freedom of Necessity* (London, 1949); see section entitled "Marxist Studies"; — as well as a large general history of science which exhibits a Marxist influence: *Science in History* (New York, 1965). The Hessen-Marxist thesis has been challenged by two eminent British historians: G. N. Clark, *Science and Social Welfare in the Age of Newton* (Oxford, 1949); A. Rupert

Hall, *Ballistics in the Seventeenth Century* (Cambridge, 1952).

Edgar Zilsel, with his scholar-craftsman theory, stands midway between Hessen's dogmatism and Merton's attempt to make an objective study in the sociology of science. For a complete list of Zilsel's writings see A. C. Keller, "Zilsel, the Artisans, and the Idea of Progress in the Renaissance," *Journal of the History of Ideas,* XI, no. 2 (1950). Zilsel's investigations are antedated by Leonardo Olschki's study of the relationship between Italian craftsmen, thinkers, and scientists: *Galilei und seine Zeit* (Halle, 1927). The scholar-craftsman theory has been perceptively criticized by A. Rupert Hall: "The Scholar and the Craftsman in the Scientific Revolution" in *Critical Problems in the History of Science,* ed. M. Clagett (Madison, 1959).

For over twenty-five years Merton's work provided the classic statement on the relationship of science and society in seventeenth-century England. Recently the British historian Christopher Hill published a book which may be read as a companion volume to Merton's study: *Intellectual Origins of the English Revolution* (Oxford, 1965). Hill traces intellectual origins of the mid-seventeenth-century English revolution which he sees as simultaneously religious, political, social, scientific, and economic. The extensive historical literature engendered by, and relevant to, the Merton-Weber thesis is conveniently located in the text and annotations of a series of reviews, articles, and debates growing out of Hill's book. See Hill, Hugh F. Kearney, Theodore K. Rabb, *et al.* in *Past and Present:* nos. 27, 28, 29 (1964); nos. 30, 31, 32 (1965); no. 33 (1966). Special mention must be made of Richard S. Westfall's *Science and Religion in Seventeenth-Century England* (New Haven, 1958) and Robert W. Green's survey *Protestantism and Capitalism: The Weber Thesis and Its Critics* (Boston, 1959).

During the twenty-seven-year period demarcated by the major publications of Merton and Hill, historians of British culture and society have been interested in the interrelationship of Protestantism and science in seventeenth-century England. Continental Protestantism, except for its bearing on the English scene, has not elicited the same interest. It is difficult, therefore, to test the validity of the Protestant interpretation by comparing the English example with a similar situation in a Protestant country or region in Europe. The first scholarly examination of Protestantism and science in seventeenth-century Europe was made by Alphonse de Candolle with his statistical study of the religious affiliations of the members of the early scientific organizations: *Histoire des Sciences et des Savants depuis Deux Siècles* (Geneva, 1873). The Protestant influence on Belgian science has been explored by Jean Pelseneer in a series of short articles: "L'Origine Protestante de la science moderne," *Lychnos* (1946–47); "Les Influences dans l'Histoire des Sciences," *Archives Internationales d'Histoire des Sciences,* I, no. 3 (1948); and "La Réforme et l'origine de la science moderne," *Revue de l'Université de Bruxelles,* (July-August, 1954). A British historian of science, Stephen F. Mason, has issued a two-part survey of developments in England and on the Continent: "The Scientific Revolution and the Protestant Reformation, I–II," *Annals of Science,* IX, nos. 1, 2 (1953). Finally, one should consult Robert K. Merton, "Puritanism, Pietism, and Science," *Social Theory and Social Structure* (Glencoe, 1963). This piece concludes with a very useful "Bibliographical Postscript."

The Catholic interpretation has not been actively pursued by scholars, but the medievalists have bolstered the Catholic contention that their religious beliefs and theology were crucial to the birth of modern science. This is not to say that the medievalists are all Catholic apologists; rather, any objective defense of medieval science and thought can be cited as evidence by the supporters of the Catholic interpretation.

Feuer stands alone in his rejection of all religious influence and his espousal of the psychological interpretation. The reactions of four historians of science and one sociologist to the Feuer thesis are to be found in the following critical reviews of his book: I. Bernard Cohen, *New York Times Book Review* (June, 1963); Charles C. Gillispie, *Science* (July 19, 1963); A. Rupert Hall, *Scientific American* (August, 1963); Donald Fleming, *Isis,* LVI (Fall, 1965); Joseph Ben-David, *American Journal of Sociology,* LXIX, no. 6 (1964).

Lynn Thorndike's *A History of Magic and Experimental Science,* 8 vols. (New York, 1923–58) is a major contribution to our understanding of modern science and the occult or "mystical" studies of earlier times. These volumes, however, are more useful as reference works than as sources of novel interpretations. Walter Pagel, who has written extensively on the history of medicine and of alchemy, recently produced a major reappraisal of the alchemist Paracelsus: *Paracelsus: an Introduction to Philosophical Medicine* (Basel, 1958). Additional material on alchemy can be found in Allen G. Debus's review article: "The Significance of the History of Early Chemistry," *Cahiers d'Histoire Mondiale,* IX, no. 1 (1965) and in his book *The English Paracelsians* (London, 1965). Astronomy and astrology are discussed by Don Cameron Allen, *The Star-Crossed Renaissance* (Durham, N. C., 1941), and Wolfgang Pauli, "The Influence of Archetypal Ideas on the Scientific Theories of Kepler" in Carl G. Jung and Wolfgang Pauli, *The Interpretation of Nature and the Psyche* (London, 1955). For a broad, philosophical treatment of this interpretation of the emergence of modern science see Ernst Cassirer, *The Individual and the Cosmos in Renaissance Philosophy* (New York, 1963), chap. IV; W. P. D. Wightman, *Science and the Renaissance,* I (Aberdeen, 1962, chap. XV; and Frances A. Yates, *Giordano Bruno and the Hermetic Tradition* (Chicago, 1964), chap. VIII.

Art historians Panofsky and Ackerman have examined the intercourse between artistic and scientific activity in the Renaissance: Erwin Panofsky, "Artist, Scientist, Genius: Notes on the 'Renaissance-Dämmerung'" in *The Renaissance: A Symposium* (New York, 1953); E. Panofsky, *Galileo as a Critic of the Arts* (The Hague, 1954); and James S. Ackerman, "Science and Visual Art" in *Seventeenth Century Science and the Arts,* ed. H. H. Rhys (Princeton, 1961). The great body of Leonardo da Vinci literature is represented here by two works; one an illustrated study of the artist's contribution to the science of anatomy, the other a critical appraisal of his influence on modern science: Charles D. O'Malley and J. B. de C. M. Saunders, *Leonardo da Vinci on the Human Body* (New York, 1952); and John Herman Randall, Jr., "The Place of Leonardo da Vinci in the Emergence of Modern Science," *Journal of the History of Ideas,* XIV, no. 2 (1953).

The internalist position has been explained and defended by Koyré and Hall in a series of books, articles, and reviews. Koyré's *Études Galiléennes,* 3 vols. (Paris, 1939), the most significant study of Galileo to be published in this century, was written from the standpoint of an internalist seeking the intellectual roots of Galilean science. Two shorter works — "Galileo and Plato," *Journal of the History of Ideas,* IV, no. 4 (1943); "Galileo and the Scientific Revolution of the XVIIth century," *Philosophical Review,* LII, no. 4 (1943) — can serve as introductions to the longer *Études.* On two other occasions Koyré wrote specifically on the emergence of modern science: "Influence of Philosophical Trends on the Formulation of Scientific Theories" in *The Validation of Scientific Theories,* ed. P. G. Frank (Boston, 1956); and "The Origins of Modern Science: A New Interpretation," *Diogenes,* no. 16 (1956). There is one final posthumous publication relevant to our topic: *Newtonian Studies* (Cambridge, Mass., 1965). Hall's attacks on the externalists are listed above; see discussions of Hessen, Zilsel, and Feuer.

An assessment of Koyré's influence upon scholarship in the history of science can be found in two pieces written by I. Bernard Cohen: I. Bernard Cohen and René Taton, "Hommage à Alexandre Koyré" in *Mélanges Alexandre Koyré,* I (Paris, 1964); and I. Bernard Cohen, "Alexandre Koyré (1892–1964), Commemoration," *Isis,* LVII (Summer, 1966).

Prior to the establishment of a definite internalist interpretation by historians of science, a group of philosophers explored the intellectual backgrounds of early modern science. A. E. Burtt's *The Metaphysical Foundation of Modern Physical Science* (London, 1932) is the most detailed of these explorations. For other examples see Ernst Cassirer *The Individual and the Cosmos in Renaissance Philosophy* (New York, 1963), chap. IV; R. G. Collingwood, *The Idea of Nature* (Oxford, 1945), part II, chap. I; Alfred North Whitehead, *Science and the Modern World* (New York, 1925), chaps. I–III. Whitehead's views on the origins of modern science have been delineated by Robert Palter: "Science and Its History in the Philosophy of Whitehead," in *Process and Divinity: The Hartshorne Festschrift,* eds. W. R. Reese and E. Freeman (Chicago, 1964).

There are several discussions of the internalist-externalist debate: Robert S. Cohen, "Alternative Interpretations of the History of Science," in *The Validation of Scientific Theories,* ed. P. G. Frank (Boston, 1956); Victor F. Lenzen, "Science and Social Context," in *Civilization* (Berkeley, 1959); S. Lilley, "Social Aspects of the History of Science," *Archives Internationales d'Histoire des Sciences,* II, no. 6 (1949); S. Lilley, "Cause & Effect in the History of Science," *Centaurus,* III, nos. 1–2 (1953); John U. Nef, "The Genesis of Industrialism and of Modern Science, 1540–1640" in *Essays in Honor of Conyers Read,* ed. N. Downs (Chicago, 1952).

One aspect of the problem of the rise of modern science has not been discussed here because it transcends the boundaries of European civilization. It is the question: Why did modern science first make its appearance in the West and not in one of the older civilizations of the East? For a tentative answer read Joseph Needham, "Poverties and Triumphs of the Chinese Scientific Tradition," in *Scientific Change,* ed. A. C. Crombie (New York, 1963).

3 4 5 6 7 8 9 10